BARNES & NOBLE BASICS™

diabetes cookbook

by Deborah Bone

BARNES
& NOBLE
BOOKS

NEW YORK

introduction

Since food and diabetes are so intimately linked, we all need to pay attention to what we eat. But that doesn't have to mean a diet that's dull or flavorless. Discovering new ingredients and experimenting with different cooking methods can be a very enjoyable, not to mention tasty, adventure for the whole family. That's where **Barnes & Noble Basics** *Diabetes Cookbook* comes in. It was written by professional chef Deborah Bone, whose husband has diabetes. She discovered how a few simple cooking techniques can turn an ordinary dish into a delicious event that just happens to be low in fat and carbohydrates. For example, instead of Eggs Benedict, which is typically loaded with cholesterol and fat, try the simple but elegant Little Breakfast Soufflés on page 24. Instead of frying your zucchini sticks, save on calories and time and bake them. See Baked Zucchini Sticks on page 46 for the easy-to-follow recipe. Everyone loves brownies: Try the Cocoa Chocolate Brownies on page 186 and save on fat and sugar.

The secret is out. You and your family can eat delicious, fulfilling meals, and even splurge occasionally, while still meeting everyone's nutritional needs. Enjoy!

Barb Chintz
Editorial Director, the **Barnes & Noble Basics**™ series

table of contents

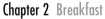

Chapter 1

Getting Started

A few simple changes in your cooking techniques can do wonders for your diet. For example, these delicious Oven-Fried Chicken Tenders (top, recipe on page 110) are baked instead of deep fried, which saves on calories and fat. Here's another healthy idea: Use phyllo pastry instead of fat-laden puff pastry. In this tempting Phyllo Beef Wellington (right, recipe on page 102), phyllo saves you calories and time.

food fundamentals
Glucose and you

There was a time when your biggest concern about sugar was one lump or two. But since you or your loved one has received a diabetes diagnosis, much of your concern now revolves around the amount of carbohydrates in your diet. Sugar, starches, vegetables, fruits, and even dairy products contain carbohydrates.

Why all this concern with carbohydrates? In your body, carbohydrates are converted to **glucose**—the fuel that energizes your body's cells. In order for it to be absorbed into the bloodstream, your pancreas needs to release insulin—a hormone that moves glucose into the body's cells or stores it for future use. But when you have diabetes, this glucose-insulin loop is not working very well. Either your pancreas does not produce enough insulin to absorb the glucose effectively (Type 1 diabetes), or your body is resisting the insulin it does supply (Type 2 diabetes). The result is the same: Glucose does not enter cells properly and remains in your blood, where it can cause, among other things, dizziness, fatigue, and unquenchable thirst.

The good news is that you can help counteract this problem by paying close attention to what you eat. The American Diabetes Association has developed two ingenious systems to help you monitor your diet. The first is called the **Exchange System**, where you monitor the types of foods you eat. For more on this see pages 12-13. The second is called **Carbohydrate Counting**. Here you count the number of carbohydrates you consume every day. For more on how this works, see pages 14-15. Both systems require that you keep a daily food diary. Sound complicated? It doesn't have to be. There are many resources out there to help you get started. One place to start is **www.MyDiabetes.com**. This free Web site provides charts and diaries you can use to track your blood glucose levels, carbohydrate intake, medication usage, and more.

what do I do now?

My husband just received a diagnosis of prediabetes. I have never heard of that before. What is does it mean?

In 2003 the American Diabetes Association came out with new guidelines for acceptable blood glucose levels. They have lowered the acceptable level of fasting blood glucose from 110 mg/dl (milligrams per deciliter) to 100 mg/dl. In the past, blood glucose levels of 110 mg/dl or more were cause for concern and usually meant something called **impaired glucose tolerance**, or IGT. (Levels of 125 mg/dl or over meant a diagnosis of diabetes.) The new level of 100 mg/dl now signals a condition called **prediabetes**. While there are no symptoms, many people with prediabetes will develop full-blown diabetes. The good news is that with proper diet and exercise, along with close monitoring by your doctor, your husband can prevent prediabetes from developing into diabetes.

I can't even stay on a regular diet, so how am I supposed to deal with a restrictive diabetic diet?

Relax! There is actually no such thing as a diabetic diet. You can still enjoy the foods you love—all you have to do is keep an eye on your intake.

How do I find a diet for my diabetes that matches my lifestyle?

The best person to see is a registered dietitian (R.D.) who also is a certified diabetes educator (C.D.E.). The services of an R.D. for diabetes management are covered by Medicare and may be covered by your insurance company. Your doctor will probably refer you to a registered dietitian he or she recommends for patients with diabetes. Or you can find a dietitian on your own through the Yellow Pages, by contacting the American Dietetic Association (visit **www.eatright.org** or call 800-877-1600, ext. 5000, for the names of dietitians in your area), or by asking your insurance carrier for names of approved providers.

eating for your health
How food works when you have diabetes

While all types of food can raise blood glucose levels, not all foods are created equal. Some offer something we all need: better nutrition. We all need to make the best food choices we can. Here's a basic primer on nutrition to help inform your decisions.

Carbohydrates give you energy. Grain foods, fruits, vegetables, legumes (dried peas, beans, and lentils), and dairy products all supply carbohydrates, plus vitamins and minerals. Foods high in sugar, such as desserts and nondiet soft drinks, should be consumed sparingly because they supply carbohydrates without many other important nutrients. (Moreover, they will make your blood sugar soar.) High-fiber carbohydrate foods— whole-grain breads, bran cereals, legumes, vegetables, and fruits—are a wise choice because they make you feel full, provide nutrients, and can help control your blood sugar and blood cholesterol. (One gram of carbohydrate equals four calories.)

Protein helps maintain muscles and organs in the body. Your diet should include modest portions of protein foods, such as meats, poultry, fish, dairy products, nuts, eggs, and legumes. If your blood sugar is difficult to control, your dietitian may recommend that you eat more protein and fat and fewer portions of carbohydrate foods. (One gram of protein equals four calories.)

Fat is present in meats, dairy products, oils, nuts, butter, and margarine. It is another source of energy. Your body also uses fat to manufacture hormones. Some fats are better than others. Monounsaturated fats, found in nuts, olive oil, canola oil, and avocados, are better for your heart because they do not make blood cholesterol go up. Polyunsaturated fat, in vegetable oils like corn oil and safflower oil, is the next healthiest. Saturated fat, found in higher-fat meat and regular dairy products, should be limited. Since all fats supply a lot of calories—one gram of fat is nine calories—it's best to limit your fat intake.

Cholesterol is a fatlike substance used to form cell membranes and to make hormones like estrogen and testosterone. Meat, poultry, seafood, dairy products, and eggs supply cholesterol; it is not found in plant foods. The liver also makes cholesterol. A diet high in saturated fat can make blood cholesterol levels go up. Limiting saturated fats and including higher cholesterol foods only in moderation can help control blood cholesterol levels. This is important because high cholesterol has been associated with an increased risk of heart disease, and heart disease is a common complication of diabetes.

Fiber comes in two forms. Soluble fiber, which gives you energy and may lower your blood cholesterol, is found in barley, legumes, citrus fruits, apples, and carrots. Insoluble fiber softens stools, helping to prevent diverticulosis, hemorrhoids, and constipation. It's found in whole wheat, bran, root vegetables, and fruits with edible seeds. Foods rich in fiber also contain important vitamins and minerals and are low in calories and fat.

First Person Insight: *Let Me Eat Cake*

Nothing aggravates me more than when my friends tell me how to eat. After I mentioned my diabetes to one dear friend, she started making comments about what I ate whenever we met for lunch. The last time we got together, I ordered cake. She all but screamed at me. I was so mad I told her to mind her own business. Then she burst into tears! I had to explain that even though I have diabetes I can still eat sugar every now and then in moderation. I can adjust for the cake with extra insulin later. She hasn't said a word about my diet choices since.

—Anna T., Niagara Falls, NY

using exchanges
Learn how to trade with food groups

There's a little of the natural-born trader in all of us, and the classic tool for planning your diet cleverly takes advantage of that. The exchange system, as it's called, helps you get the nutrition you need while controlling your blood sugar. Your daily food intake is divided into a certain number of servings from the three main exchange groups, then divided into meals and snacks. Think of the exchange system like a budget: You get a certain amount of "money"—in this case, exchanges—to spend on each type of food.

Foods are grouped according to the amount of carbohydrates, protein, and fat they contain. The largest group is the Carbohydrate Group; it includes starches (bread, cereal, grain foods, and starchy vegetables such as peas and corn), fruit, milk, nonstarchy vegetables, and other carbohydrates, such as desserts. The Meat and Meat Substitutes Group is divided into very lean, lean, medium-fat, and high-fat foods. For heart health, choose primarily from the very lean and lean lists. The Fat Group includes foods with monounsaturated, polyunsaturated, saturated, and trans fats. All fats are high in calories; as such, they should be limited.

Each meal should contain one or two servings from each group—for instance, one meat and one grain food, perhaps a slice of bread with a small pat of butter, as your allowance of fat, along with vegetables and/or fruit. The idea is that as long as you eat the recommended portion sizes, you will be getting a healthy—and not too large—amount of each, and not too much of any one group. You can also exchange servings within each group—say a serving of peas instead of a slice of bread, or low-fat cottage cheese instead of meat. Or you might have a slice of pizza and get all three groups in one food. The point is, you get to decide. Your dietitian can give you a list of foods and exchanges.

EXCHANGE LISTS VS. THE FOOD PYRAMID

Does the diabetes exchange diet plan conflict with the government's Food Guide Pyramid?

Not at all. In fact, the two are very similar. Each recommends that a healthy daily diet include:

- 3 servings of vegetables, including starchy vegetables

- 2 servings of fruit

- 2 servings of low-fat or fat-free milk

- about 6 ounces of meat or meat substitutes, including beans

- small amounts of fat and sugar

Unlike the standard pyramid, the diabetes exchange system groups grains, beans, and starchy vegetables together because they supply similar amounts of carbohydrates per serving. (A diabetes pyramid has been developed.) Both the exchange system and the pyramid recommend selecting whole-grain foods as part of your diet.

Here's a sample of foods and portions that equal one exchange on the diabetes starch list:

Bread	1 slice
English muffin	1/2
Cob of corn	1 medium
Grits	1/2 cup
Cooked pasta	1/2 cup
Cereal	1/2 cup
Soda crackers	6 crackers

counting carbohydrates
Let carb choices be your guide

Not so many years ago, people with diabetes who took insulin had to eat the same amount of food at about the same time every day. This made for a simple system that helped to keep blood sugar in the normal range, but many people had difficulty sticking to such a strict regimen and wound up with blood sugar that was consistently too high. Carbohydrate counting, introduced widely in the mid-1990s, can help you better control blood sugar by tying carbs to insulin intake on a sliding scale—15 grams of carbohydrate for every dose of insulin.

With carbohydrate counting, each 15 grams of carhobyrate is the equivalent of one **carb choice**. So, for example, if you are allowed 150 grams of carbohydrate a day, you can have 10 carb choices per day. You might decide to have three of these at breakfast—in the form of 3/4 cup unsweetened cereal, 3/4 cup blueberries, and a cup of low-fat milk, each of which equals one carb choice—and then three for lunch, one for a snack, and three for dinner. Once you get a handle on counting carbs, your meal choices are virtually endless and your blood sugar will be much easier to control since your diabetes medicine is taken in direct proportion to your carbohydrate intake.

Your doctor or diabetes educator will give you a carbohydrate goal for the day and for each meal, along with a blood sugar goal. Most adults consume around 200 grams of carbohydrates a day, or 13 carb choices. (That amounts to some 800 calories that go toward carbohydrates. Your other daily calories come from fat and protein. The average person consumes about 2,000 calories a day.)

SAMPLE PAGES FROM A CARB-COUNTING DIET

Daily goal: 10 carb choices, or 150 grams of carbohydrate

MEAL	FOOD	CARB CHOICES USED
Breakfast	3/4 cup cereal	1
	3/4 cup blueberries	1
	1 cup low-fat milk	1
Lunch	1 cup chili	1
	1 cup salad	1
	1 orange	1
Snack	1 granola bar	1
Dinner	1 medium baked potato	2
	2 cups salad greens	1
	1 tablespoon dressing	0
	4 oz. grilled chicken	0
	Total	**10 carb choices**

cooking tips to lose weight

Ten smart ways to keep the the pounds off

Maintaining a proper body weight is vital to your health, whether or not you have diabetes. It's never too late to start making healthy choices in the foods you eat. And while you are at it, make changes in how you cook. Here are ten tips that are sure to help you cut calories and fat without even feeling it.

1. Enhance the protein you eat by tenderizing it before cooking. Tenderizing (pounding the meat with a mallet) makes a little bit of meat look bigger. It also makes it cook faster. (Thinner pieces of meat are also quicker to freeze and thaw.) You can also extend your meat by combining it with an assortment of vegetables, such as Stir-Baked Beef and Green Beans (see page 104).

2. "Oven-fry" instead of pan- or deep-frying. You'll get crisp, moist, flavorful foods with very little fat. Lightly coat the breaded food with cooking spray and cook in a very hot oven (450° to 500°F) for 5 to 7 minutes, depending on thickness. (Try Oven-Fried Chicken Tenders; see page 110.)

3. Use nonstick skillets and use cooking spray whenever possible. Coating a nonstick skillet or wok with cooking spray saves 45 calories for every teaspoon of fat you eliminate. Add a little broth half way through sautéing; this creates steam that helps cook vegetables tender crisp. Coating meats, breaded vegetables, and low-fat pastries with cooking spray before roasting or baking helps brown them nicely without adding extra fat.

4. Roast meats or poultry on a rack so that the fat drips away into the roasting pan. When roasting chicken, leave the skin on during cooking since it keeps the meat moist and tender. Remove the skin before serving.

5. Roast fresh vegetables to concentrate their flavor. (It's a nice alternative to steamed vegetables.) If you're cooking for a few people, just toss the cut vegetables with a little olive oil and seasoning, spread on a baking sheet, and bake in a hot oven (450°F) for 20 to 30 minutes. They should be softened and moderately browned at the edges.

6. Use cornstarch to thicken sauces instead of cream or flour. One tablespoon of cornstarch thickens one cup of liquid to the consistency of pancake syrup. The liquid must be brought to a boil to achieve its maximum thickness. Cornstarch is twice as powerful a thickener as flour, so you will use half as much. Moreover, this thickening method adds far fewer calories than thickening with butter or cream.

7. Save calories on high-fat goodies like nuts, olives, and avocado by chopping them into bits and sprinkling them on a dish for flavor.

8. Use a vegetable peeler to cut cheese. With a good peeler, you can shave very thin slices of good cheeses for a snack, sandwich, or salad. You'll get flavor without as much fat.

9. Use low-fat phyllo dough. It's a great alternative to pie crusts or puff pastry in many baked desserts. Use butter-flavored cooking spray rather than melted butter between the delicate sheets of pastry. Phyllo bakes up crisp and flaky with a fraction of the fat, calories, and carbs of other pastries. Try Phyllo Beef Wellington on page 102.

10. Eat fruit-based desserts. Fruit is naturally low in fat. If you crave pastry, use crumble toppings in fruit desserts instead of a pastry.

questions and answers about diabetes

What is the glycemic index, and should I avoid foods with a high glycemic index?

The glycemic index (GI) measures how high your blood sugar is likely to go after eating a particular food. In general, high-fiber foods, such as oatmeal or whole-wheat bread, have a lower GI than do processed lower-fiber foods like white bread. Sugar, however, has a lower GI than do many other foods. The GI is not very useful for planning your diet.

I heard those low-carbohydrate diets are great for losing weight. They sound perfect for people with diabetes, right?

Yes and no. Yes, a high-protein, low-carbohydrate diet can lead to pretty dramatic weight loss, as well as to an overall reduction in blood sugar levels, but all that extra protein can make the kidneys work harder than usual. Since people with diabetes are at risk for developing kidney disease, this is a concern. Also, the low-carbohydrate diet is very unforgiving and many people who try it and go off it gain all the weight back and more. You want a well balanced diet that is low in calories for a slow and steady weight loss of, say, three to four pounds a month. Besides, a balanced diet is much easier to maintain than a restrictive one.

My teenager has Type 2 diabetes and loves sports, but he often doesn't watch what he eats before practice. What can I do?

Ideally, all diabetics should check their blood sugar prior to exercise. Getting a teenager to comply with any rule can be difficult; the same goes for diabetic teenagers. For this reason, you should talk to his coach and explain the need for blood sugar testing and that exercise should be avoided if his blood sugar levels are too low. Talk to your son about the importance of a healthy carbohydrate snack before practice.

I am four months pregnant and have just been told I have gestational diabetes. What should I do?

About four percent of pregnant women develop diabetes during pregnancy, even though their blood sugar had previously been normal. Your doctor, dietitian, and diabetes educator will work with you to develop a meal, exercise, and medication plan to help keep your blood sugar under control during pregnancy. Women with gestational diabetes are more likely to develop Type 2 diabetes later in life, so take preventive measures after your pregnancy: Lose any extra weight you gained. Eat plenty of fruits and vegetables. Find activities that you like and that fit your daily routine, such as walking, mother-and-baby exercise classes, or swimming.

Now where do I go?

WEB SITES

American Association of Diabetes Educators
www.diabeteseducator.org

www.MyDiabetes.com
Resources include a handy online food and insulin diary.

www.mendosa.com
Rick Mendosa's comprehensive diabetes self-education site.

BOOKS

The Complete Guide to Carbohydrate Counting
by Hope S. Warshaw and
Karmeen Kulkarni

*The Diabetes Food and Nutrition Bible:
A Complete Guide to Planning, Shopping,
Cooking, and Eating*
by Hope S. Warshaw, Robyn Webb, and
Graham Kerr

*Diabetes Meal Planning Made Easy: How to
Put the Food Pyramid to Work for Your Busy
Lifestyle*
by Hope S. Warshaw

Barnes and Noble Health Basics: Diabetes
by Paul Heltzel

Chapter 2

Breakfast

Don't skimp on breakfast—you need it to start your day off right. Here are some very tempting ideas to get you going in the morning: Banana Pancakes with Peanut Butter Syrup (top) and Raisin Oat Scones (right).

baked French toast with sugar-free syrup

The cook won't get stuck at the stove flipping slices in this delicious baked version of French toast

Serves: 3
Prep Time: 10 minutes
Cooking Time: 12-15 minutes

INGREDIENTS

Cooking spray

1 cup low-fat milk

2 eggs

1 egg white

¼ cup Splenda

½ teaspoon cinnamon

6 slices stale bread (or fresh bread lightly toasted)

3 tablespoons sugar-free syrup or spoonful of fruit spread

SUGAR-FREE SYRUP
½ cup, plus 1 tablespoon water

1 teaspoon cornstarch

2 tablespoons fruit spread (no sugar added)

1 tablespoon Splenda

---

1. **PREHEAT** oven to 350°F. **COAT** a cookie sheet with cooking spray.

2. **WHISK** together in a large bowl the milk, eggs, egg white, Splenda and cinnamon. **CUT** bread slices in half to make 12 pieces. **DIP** bread slices 2 to 3 at a time in the batter and let them soak 10 seconds.

3. Arrange soaked bread on the prepared cookie sheet and **BAKE** 12 to 15 minutes. Carefully flip the slices halfway through cooking. Serve warm with sugar-free syrup or a spoonful of fruit spread.

SUGAR-FREE SYRUP
Serves: 3   Prep Time: 1 minute   Cooking Time: 10 minutes

1. Bring ½ cup water to a boil.

2. **ADD** 1 teaspoon cornstarch dissolved in 1 tablespoon cold water and return to a boil. The cornstarch and water will thicken to a syrupy texture.

3. **STIR** 2 tablespoons of your favorite no-sugar-added fruit spread plus 1 tablespoon Splenda into the boiling liquid and stir until dissolved. **PUREE** the mixture in the blender if desired. Cool and serve.

Baked French toast with sugar-free syrup
NUTRITIONAL VALUE PER SERVING

Calories	230	Total Fat	6g
Carbohydrates	31g	Saturated Fat	2g
Protein	12g	Cholesterol	145mg
Fiber	1g	Sodium	370mg

Exchanges: 2 carbohydrates, 1 medium-fat meat
Carb Choices: 2

Sugar-free syrup by itself
NUTRITIONAL VALUE PER SERVING

Calories	35	Total Fat	0g
Carbohydrates	8g	Saturated Fat	0g
Protein	0g	Cholesterol	0mg
Fiber	0g	Sodium	0mg

Exchanges: ½ other carbohydrate
Carb Choices: ½

what do I do now?

I don't like sugar-free syrups very much. What else can I serve with my pancakes and French toast?

You can use real syrup, but you have to check the carb counts and perhaps sacrifice having more French toast in order to enjoy the real syrup. Alternately, you can make your own sugar-free syrup, and it will be tastier than the kind you buy in the store (see recipe opposite page).

ARTIFICIAL SWEETENERS

Artificial sweeteners are substances that make foods taste sweet without adding calories or carbohydrates. There are several on the market— while each one sweetens foods, they are chemically different and act differently when used in cooking:

Aspartame is sold as **Nutrasweet** or **Equal**. It is about 200 times sweeter than sugar. Aspartame is a good way to sweeten cold or warm foods and drinks, but it breaks down when heated, losing its sweetness and becoming bitter. For this reason you should not cook with Aspartame.

Saccharine, a chemical sweetener that is 300 to 500 times sweeter than sugar, is sold under the brand name **Sweet 'n Low**. Saccharine does not break down at high temperatures, thus making cooking and baking possible, but because it is less dense than sugar, it does not bring the candied texture to baked desserts that sugar does. Saccharine sweeteners also have a distinct aftertaste.

Sucralose, sold under the brand name **Splenda**, is formulated for cooking and baking. It substitutes in equal volume for sugar; in other words, one cup of Splenda equals one cup of sugar. It is very light in texture so it does not produce the dense, sticky consistency that sugar does in some desserts, but it has practically no aftertaste.

little breakfast soufflés

Not soufflés in the strictest sense, these easy egg white cups puff beautifully and will impress any egg gourmet

Serves: 3

Prep Time: 10 minutes

Cooking Time: 12-15 minutes

INGREDIENTS

Cooking spray

1 egg

2 egg whites

1/3 cup all-purpose flour

1/3 cup low-fat milk

Pinch of salt

3 tablespoons reduced-fat Swiss or cheddar cheese, grated

2 tablespoons diced deli ham

1. **PREHEAT** the oven to 400°F. **COAT** 6 muffin tins with cooking spray.

2. **WHISK** vigorously in a bowl the egg, egg whites, flour, milk, and salt.

3. **FILL** each muffin tin 2/3 full with batter and sprinkle with 1/6 of the cheese and 1/6 of the diced deli ham.

4. **BAKE** 12 to 15 minutes until the soufflés are golden brown and beautifully puffed. Serve immediately.

Just a bit of diced ham and cheese turn these easy-to-make egg soufflés into a flavorful feast while saving on fat and calories.

24

what do I do now?

Are egg whites really that much better for me than whole eggs?

Well, take a look at the numbers and decide for yourself:

	Whole Egg	Egg White
Calories:	75	17
Fat:	5 g	0 g
Protein:	6 g	3.5 g
Cholesterol:	212 mg	0 mg
Carbohydrates:	.6 g	0 g

Figures come from the USDA's National Nutrient Database for Standard Reference

Can I cook with egg substitutes instead of real eggs?

Yes. Egg substitutes, such as Egg Beaters, are readily available in grocery stores. They're made from egg whites with other nutrients and natural coloring added. Usually 1/4 cup of egg substitute is equal to one egg. Read the directions on the carton for the best results.

Little breakfast soufflés
NUTRITIONAL VALUE PER SERVING

Calories	120	Total Fat	4g
Carbohydrates	12g	Saturated Fat	2g
Protein	9g	Cholesterol	80mg
Fiber	0g	Sodium	125mg

Exchanges: 1 carbohydrates, 1 lean meat
Carb Choices: 1

basic bran muffins

Add a variety of toppings before baking to create a delicious muffin assortment

Serves: 6

Prep Time: 20 minutes

Cooking Time: 15-18 minutes

INGREDIENTS

Cooking spray

1 cup all-purpose flour

4 tablespoons Splenda

2 teaspoons baking powder

Pinch of salt

1/3 cup bran cereal (such as All Bran)

2 eggs

1/4 cup low-fat milk

1/4 cup unsweetened applesauce

2 tablespoons vegetable oil

1 teaspoon vanilla extract

1. **PREHEAT** oven to 400°F. Lightly **COAT** a 12-cup muffin pan with cooking spray.

2. **SIFT** together flour, Splenda, baking powder, and salt in a medium-size bowl. Add bran cereal and mix well.

3. In a separate large bowl, **WHISK** thoroughly eggs, milk, applesauce, oil, and vanilla.

4. Gently **FOLD** the dry mixture into the wet mixture. **MIX** gently until ingredients are just combined. A few lumps are fine.

5. **FILL** coated muffin tins 2/3 full. At this point you can **TOP** the muffins with a variety of flavorings, such as grated apples and cinnamon, diced bananas and walnuts, chopped raisins and cranberries, or semisweet chocolate chips and pecans.

6. **BAKE** 15 to 18 minutes until the tops of the muffins spring back when gently pressed. Cool and serve.

NUTRITIONAL VALUE FOR TWO MUFFINS			
Calories	170	Total Fat	7g
Carbohydrates	21g	Saturated Fat	1g
Protein	5g	Cholesterol	70mg
Fiber	2g	Sodium	170mg

Exchanges: 1 1/2 carbohydrates, 1 fat
Carb Choices: 1 1/2

what do I do now?

Raisins are so small to begin with, why do I have to chop them up?

Raisins, while tasty and full of iron and potassium, are relatively high in calories and carbohydrates. Chopping them into smaller pieces will give you flavor and texture without running up your blood sugar.

Why is bran cereal so "good" for you?

Bran cereal is higher in fiber and lower in calories and carbohydrates per volume than most other breakfast cereals. Bran cereal also has a low glycemic index (see page 18), which means it won't cause spikes in your blood sugar.

raisin oat scones

Make your own scones for a scrumptious brunch or teatime treat

Serves: 8

Prep Time: 20 minutes

Cooking Time: 15-18 minutes

INGREDIENTS

Cooking spray

1 cup all-purpose flour

3 tablespoons Splenda

2 tablespoons baking powder

Pinch of salt

1/2 cup oats

3 tablespoons cold butter or margarine, chopped into small pieces

3/4 cup raisins, chopped into small pieces

1 egg

1/4 cup very cold buttermilk

1/4 cup plain fat-free yogurt

1 teaspoon vanilla extract

1. **PREHEAT** oven to 400°F and lightly **COAT** a cookie sheet with cooking spray.

2. **SIFT** into a large bowl the flour, Splenda, baking powder, and salt. Add oats and mix well.

3. Work the butter into the flour mixture with your hands, rubbing the butter and flour between your fingers until it looks like coarse bread crumbs. **ADD** the chopped raisins. Mix to combine.

4. In a separate bowl, thoroughly **WHISK** the egg, buttermilk, yogurt, and vanilla until slightly frothy.

5. **POUR** the buttermilk mixture into the flour mixture. Stir just until the ingredients come together in a soft, wet dough. Let the dough sit for one minute, then turn the dough out onto a floured work surface.

6. **KNEAD** the dough gently with your fingertips to form a ball. With a floured rolling pin, gently flatten the dough into a sheet 3/4-inch thick. Fold the dough in half and gently roll again into a 3/4-inch sheet. **REPEAT** the gentle "fold and roll" procedure two more times.

7. With a sharp knife, **TRIM** the edges of the dough to make a square. Cut the dough in half vertically then horizontally to make 4 quarters. Cut the dough diagonally both ways to make 8 triangles. Cut each triangle in half to make a total of 16 small triangular scones.

8. With a spatula, gently **LIFT** the scones, still attached to each other, onto the cookie sheet. **BAKE** 15 to 18 minutes until golden. Cool and serve.

Raisin scones are the perfect make-ahead breakfast for a family on the go.

NUTRITIONAL VALUE FOR TWO SCONES

Calories	190	Total Fat	4.5g
Carbohydrates	32g	Saturated Fat	2g
Protein	5g	Cholesterol	35mg
Fiber	2g	Sodium	320mg

Exchanges: 1 1/2 carbohydrates, 1 fruit, 1 fat
Carb Choices: 2

TIPS FOR PERFECT SCONES

Beautiful biscuits and scones are an art! Here are a few tips: Combine the margarine well, but not so well that it melts in the flour. You want tiny pieces of margarine scattered throughout the flour so that when they melt they release steam to help your tender biscuits rise. Also, keep the milk cold. This keeps the butter or margarine from melting before it hits the oven. Finally, use a sharp edge to cut the dough. A dull one seals the edges so the biscuits don't rise as much. Putting biscuits close to each other helps them rise higher, but if you want browned edges, leave them apart.

mushroom and pork tenderloin on toast

Inspired by North Carolina "biscuits and gravy," this is breakfast comfort food at its hearty best

Serves: 4

Prep Time: 15 minutes

Cooking Time: 20 minutes

INGREDIENTS

1 lean pork tenderloin, about 12-16 ounces

Salt and pepper to taste

2 teaspoons olive oil

2 cups mushrooms, sliced

1 teaspoon poultry seasoning

1/2 teaspoon ground sage

1/2 teaspoon ground thyme

3 teaspoons cornstarch

1 cup low-sodium beef broth

1/2 cup low-fat milk

8 slices whole-wheat toast

1. **TRIM** extra fat and silverskin from the tenderloin (see next page). Slice the tenderloin into medallions 1/2-inch thick. Pound the medallions between two sheets of plastic wrap using a mallet or a rolling pin until medallions are 1/4-inch thick. **SEASON** lightly with salt and pepper and set aside.

2. **HEAT** skillet over medium-high heat until a drop of water "dances" over the surface. Add 1 teaspoon olive oil to coat the surface. **COOK** flattened pork medallions 1 minute on each side. Set aside.

3. **ADD** 1 teaspoon olive oil to the skillet. Add the mushrooms and **COOK** about 4 to 5 minutes until they are softened and slightly browned. Add poultry seasoning, sage, and thyme. Add the cornstarch and stir to coat the mushrooms.

4. **ADD** the beef broth. Bring to a boil, stirring frequently. When the gravy has thickened to your liking, reduce the heat to medium and add the milk.

5. **COOK** the gravy 3 to 5 more minutes until it has returned to a low boil and has rethickened. Taste and adjust the seasoning. Return the cooked pork and any collected juices to the gravy. Serve over whole-wheat toast.

NUTRITIONAL VALUE PER SERVING			
Calories	300	Total Fat	9g
Carbohydrates	31g	Saturated Fat	2g
Protein	27g	Cholesterol	50mg
Fiber	4g	Sodium	370mg

Exchanges: 2 carbohydrates, 1/2 vegetable, 3 lean meats
Carb Choices: 2

what do I do now?

How do you trim the "silverskin" off a tenderloin?

Tenderloin is tender, but silverskin is not. Silverskin is a membrane that covers the muscle, and it tends to shrink and toughen under heat, so the meat around it cooks unevenly. It's really thin and silvery and looks almost shiny in the light. To remove it, start at the smaller end of the tenderloin and carefully slip the tip of a very sharp knife under the silverskin and gently work your knife down the tenderloin, with your knife angled slightly up.

First Person Disaster: *Low-Carb Solution*

When I would go home to Virginia, I couldn't wait for my mom's sausage cream gravy over biscuits. There was nothing on earth like it! But since I developed Type I diabetes in my early twenties, I found that it makes my blood sugar go through the roof and I feel terrible all day. I figured out that the combination of carbohydrates in the milk and flour used to make the gravy, plus the carbs in the biscuits and the fat in the sausage, work together to spike my blood sugar and keep it up. I finally figured out a way to lower the carbs by using mostly broth instead of milk, cornstarch instead of flour, and lean meats rather than sausage. I shared my findings with my mom and we both agree mushroom and pork tenderloin on toast fits the bill perfectly.

—Paula D., San Francisco, CA

sweet potato pancakes with orange honey syrup

Light and fluffy with a hint of autumn spice, these pancakes are delicious (not to mention loaded with Vitamin A)

Serves: 4

Prep Time: 12 minutes

Cooking Time: 12 minutes

INGREDIENTS

1 cup mashed sweet potato

1/2 cup all-purpose flour

1 1/2 teaspoons baking powder

1/8 teaspoon ground nutmeg

1/8 teaspoon cinnamon

Pinch of salt

1/2 cup low-fat milk

2 teaspoons vegetable oil

1 egg

1 egg white

Cooking spray

2 tablespoons orange honey syrup

ORANGE HONEY SYRUP

1 tablespoon honey

1 tablespoon orange juice (any sort will do)

2 tablespoons water

2 teaspoons margarine

1. **THAW** frozen sweet potato and measure out one cup. Or **PIERCE** a fresh sweet potato several times with a fork and microwave for 5 minutes until soft. Split the sweet potato and scoop out the flesh to measure 1 cup.

2. **MIX** flour, baking powder, nutmeg, cinnamon, and salt in a bowl.

3. **MASH** the sweet potato (once it is slightly cooled) with milk, oil, egg, and egg white in a separate bowl and **WHISK** until smooth.

4. **FOLD** the flour mixture into the sweet potato mixture and let sit 2 minutes.

5. **HEAT** a nonstick skillet or griddle and coat lightly with cooking spray. Drop 1/4 cup of batter to form pancake and cook until bubbles form and the edges of the pancake look dry. Flip the pancake and **COOK** 1 minute longer. Keep the pancakes warm in a low-temperature oven and then serve with orange honey syrup.

ORANGE HONEY SYRUP
Serves: 4   Prep Time: 1 minute   Cooking Time: 10-15 seconds

1. **COMBINE** all ingredients in a microwave-safe bowl.

2. Microwave 10 to 15 seconds.

3. **MIX** well and serve.

what do I do now?

How much honey can diabetics eat? Can I substitute honey or other "natural" sweeteners for sugar?

Honey is a great natural sweetener and can be used as part of a healthy diet. But the calories and carbohydrates in honey count in your daily intake just like those in granulated sugar. Here's how honey compares to several types of sugars and syrups in calories and carbohydrates.

One tablespoon of...	Calories	Carbohydrates
honey	64	17.3 g
granulated sugar	47	12.8 g
brown sugar	52	13.5 g
powdered sugar	29	7.5 g
pure maple syrup	52	13.4 g
pancake syrup	47	12.3 g
dietetic syrup	25	7.3 g
light corn syrup	59	15.9 g

Figures come from the USDA National Nutrient Database for Standard Reference

Sweet potato pancakes with orange honey syrup
NUTRITIONAL VALUE PER SERVING

Calories	200	Total Fat	4.5g
Carbohydrates	34g	Saturated Fat	1g
Protein	6g	Cholesterol	55mg
Fiber	2g	Sodium	240mg

Exchanges: 2 carbohydrates, 1/2 lean meat, 1/2 fat
Carb Choices: 2

Orange honey syrup by itself
NUTRITIONAL VALUE PER SERVING

Calories	35	Total Fat	2g
Carbohydrates	5g	Saturated Fat	0g
Protein	0g	Cholesterol	0mg
Fiber	0g	Sodium	20mg

Exchanges: 1/2 other carbohydrate, 1/2 fat
Carb Choices: 1/2

banana pancakes with peanut butter syrup

Peanut butter and banana—it's a combination that brings out the kid in all of us

Serves: 4

Prep Time: 10 minutes

Cooking Time: 12 minutes

INGREDIENTS

1/3 cup all-purpose flour

1 1/2 tablespoons Splenda

1 1/2 teaspoon baking powder

Pinch of salt

1/3 cup mashed banana (about 1 large banana)

1 egg

1 egg white

2 teaspoons reduced-fat peanut butter (smooth or crunchy)

1/3 cup low-fat milk

Cooking spray

3 tablespoons peanut butter syrup (see recipe)

PEANUT BUTTER SYRUP

1 teaspoon margarine

1 1/2 tablespoon reduced-fat peanut butter

1/4 cup water

1 teaspoon Splenda

1. **SIFT** flour, Splenda, baking powder, and salt in a bowl and set aside.

2. **MASH** banana, egg, and egg white in a separate bowl.

3. **ADD** peanut butter to banana mixture. **WHISK** until mixture is fluffy and the peanut butter is fully incorporated.

4. **ADD** milk and whisk until smooth.

5. **FOLD** the flour mixture into the wet mixture. Do not overmix.

6. Let stand two minutes while you **HEAT** a nonstick skillet or griddle pan over medium heat.

7. **COAT** pan very lightly with cooking spray. Pour scant 1/4 cup of batter into heated pan to form each pancake. Cook until bubbles form in the batter and edges of the pancake appear dry. Flip pancake and cook 1 minute longer or until done. Serve with peanut butter syrup.

PEANUT BUTTER SYRUP

Serves: 4   Prep Time: 1 minute   Cooking Time: 10-15 seconds

1. **COMBINE** all ingredients in a microwave-safe bowl.

2. Microwave 10 to 15 seconds to soften all ingredients.

3. **WHISK** until smooth and serve.

Banana pancakes with peanut butter syrup
NUTRITIONAL VALUE PER SERVING

Calories	100	Total Fat	2.5g
Carbohydrates	15g	Saturated Fat	1g
Protein	5g	Cholesterol	55mg
Fiber	0g	Sodium	240mg

Exchanges: 1 fruit, 1/2 lean meat
Carb Choices: 1

The peanut butter adds a luscious flavor, not to mention
a dollop of protein, in these sure-to-please pancakes.

Peanut butter syrup by itself
NUTRITIONAL VALUE PER SERVING

Calories	40	Total Fat	3g
Carbohydrates	2g	Saturated Fat	0.5g
Protein	2g	Cholesterol	0mg
Fiber	0g	Sodium	45mg

Exchanges: 1 fat
Carb Choices: 0

Chapter 3

Snacks and Starters

Appetizers are often loaded with fat and sugar. Here is a delectable array of healthy snacks: Low-Yolk Deviled Eggs (top) and Roasted Eggplant Dip (right).

Tuscan white bean spread

This hearty dip goes great with French bread chips and crudités

Serves: 4

Prep Time: 5 minutes

Cooking Time: 5 minutes

Chilling Time: 30 minutes

INGREDIENTS

1 teaspoon olive oil

1/4 cup yellow onion, diced small

1 teaspoon garlic, chopped

1 15-ounce can cannellini beans, drained and rinsed

1/4 cup low-sodium chicken broth (water plus 1/2 teaspoon olive oil may be substituted)

1/2 tablespoon parsley, chopped

1/4 teaspoon black pepper

1/4 teaspoon salt

1. **HEAT** the olive oil in a skillet over medium heat. Add the onion and garlic and **COOK** until they have wilted and browned slightly around the edges. Cool.

2. In a blender or food processor, **PUREE** the cannellini beans and the broth. Add the onion mixture and blend until smooth.

3. Transfer to a bowl and **STIR** in the parsley, black pepper, and salt. **CHILL** at least 30 minutes before serving. Serve with baked chip medley (see page 42) or crudités.

NUTRITIONAL VALUE PER SERVING			
Calories	80	Total Fat	1.5g
Carbohydrates	13g	Saturated Fat	0g
Protein	4g	Cholesterol	0mg
Fiber	4g	Sodium	330mg

Exchanges: 1 carbohydrate, 1/2 very lean meat
Carb Choices: 1

what is it  and where do I get it?

CRUDITÉS

From the French for "rawness," crudités refer to raw vegetables that are served as an hors d'oeuvre or snack. Carrots and celery are the obvious choices. But don't forget about cucumbers, either cut in rings or long spears, and florets of cauliflower and broccoli. Radishes and grape tomatoes add a little color and some interesting textures to your crudités. Pale, yellow-tipped leaves of Belgian endive are an elegant addition; just make sure to eat them within a day of purchase to avoid bitterness.

Jicama, a root vegetable from Mexico, has crisp, sweet flesh, and tastes a bit like a fresh water chestnut. Peel the jicama before cutting it into sticks or slices to add some zip to your raw veggie snacks. And just because crudités literally mean raw, doesn't mean a few blanched veggies can't be thrown in the mix. Try dropping asparagus spears, trimmed green beans, snow peas, or sugar snap peas in rapidly boiling water for 30 seconds. Immediately plunge them in iced water to stop the cooking. They're great on a vegetable platter for company or refrigerated in a plastic container for a healthy snack any time.

low-yolk deviled eggs

Delicious as a snack or party treat, these have a fraction of the fat and cholesterol of regular deviled eggs

Serves: 6

Prep Time: 20 minutes

Cooking Time: 20 minutes

INGREDIENTS

6 hardboiled eggs

4 tablespoons canned white beans, drained and pureed in blender

1 tablespoon fat-free mayonnaise

1 tablespoon fat-free sour cream

1 teaspoon mustard

Additional flavorings and garnishes (optional)

1. PEEL the eggs. Cut them in half. Carefully remove the yolks. **RESERVE** the yolks of three eggs and discard the remaining yolks. Set aside the egg whites.

2. MASH yolks well with a fork. Mix in the white bean puree, mayonnaise, sour cream, and mustard. Add flavorings, such as curry powder, fat-free cream cheese with roasted red pepper, or grated cheddar cheese with chopped green onion, if desired. Refrigerate 30 minutes to develop flavors and firm the yolk filling.

3. SPOON yolk mixture into egg halves. Refrigerate until ready to serve. Garnish with paprika or sliced chives, if desired, and serve.

Traditional deviled eggs are usually high in fat and cholesterol, but not this variation. Here pureed white beans lend a low-fat touch.

what do I do now?

I like eggs, but I thought I shouldn't be eating them because of the high cholesterol content. Can diabetics include eggs in their diet?

Yes, you can eat eggs and they're a great source of protein. But because heart disease is often associated with diabetes, it is important that diabetics watch their cholesterol intake. You should have no more than 200 mg of cholesterol each day or the equivalent of one whole egg. If you want to eat eggs, pay careful attention to the other sources of cholesterol in your diet and try to cut down or eliminate them.

How can I keep the yolks from turning grayish when I hard-boil eggs?

The grayish-green color comes from iron in the yolk interacting with sulfur and hydrogen in the whites when heated. It's harmless, but not very attractive. You can minimize the effect by plunging the eggs in cold water as soon as they're cooked. Peeling the eggs as soon as you can will also help keep them from turning color. Finally, really fresh eggs are less apt to turn greenish around the yolks. However, really fresh eggs are harder to peel when hard-boiled than ones that have been in the refrigerator a few days.

NUTRITIONAL VALUE PER SERVING			
Calories	60	Total Fat	3g
Carbohydrates	3g	Saturated Fat	1g
Protein	5g	Cholesterol	105mg
Fiber	0g	Sodium	110mg

Exchanges: 1 lean meat
Carb Choices: 0

baked chip medley

Keep this wonderful variety of tasty, low-fat crisps around the house for snacking any time

Serves: 8

Prep Time: 10 minutes

Cooking Time: 20-30 minutes

INGREDIENTS

3 corn tortillas

Cooking spray

1/2 teaspoon salt

2 pieces whole-wheat pita bread

1 egg white

1 tablespoon water

1 teaspoon cumin

3 slices light rye bread (any good, flavorful bread can be used)

1/2 French baguette, sliced into thin rounds

1. **PREHEAT** oven to 275°F.

2. Lightly coat the tortillas with cooking spray. Sprinkle with salt. Cut each tortilla into 8 wedges. Arrange on a cookie sheet.

3. **SPLIT** the pitas completely open so you have 4 disks of bread. Lightly whisk the egg white and water in a small bowl. With a pastry brush, brush the top of each pita disk with the egg wash. Sprinkle with cumin. **CUT** each pita disk into 8 wedges. Arrange on the cookie sheet.

4. **TRIM** crusts from the rye bread. With a rolling pin, flatten the rye bread until it is uniformly cracker-thin. **CUT** the flattened rye bread into strips. Arrange the rye strips and the baguette slices on the cookie sheet with the other chips.

5. **BAKE** 20 minutes, checking after the first 10 minutes to prevent burning. The chips should be completely crisp after 20 to 25 minutes. Turn off the oven but leave the chips in if they need a little more time to crisp. Store in an airtight container. Serve as a snack or an appetizer with a variety of dips.

NUTRITIONAL VALUE PER SERVING			
Calories	100	Total Fat	1g
Carbohydrates	18g	Saturated Fat	0g
Protein	3g	Cholesterol	0mg
Fiber	2g	Sodium	320mg
Exchanges: 1 carbohydrate			
Carb Choices: 1			

chili black bean dip

Great for a casual get-together along with baked tortilla chips and your favorite salsa

Serves: 8

Prep Time: 5 minutes

Cooking Time: 30 minutes

INGREDIENTS

1 15-ounce can black beans, drained and rinsed

1/4 cup low-sodium chicken stock (water may be substituted)

1 tablespoon grated onion

1 tablespoon ketchup

1 tablespoon chili powder

1 teaspoon cumin

1. PUREE all ingredients in a blender or food processor. **CHILL** 30 minutes to develop flavors. Serve with baked chip medley (see previous page).

2. For a warm appetizer, transfer the dip to a microwaveable dish and sprinkle with 1/4 cup shredded cheese. **HEAT** one minute. **TOP** with fat-free sour cream, black olives, chopped green onions, diced tomatoes, and fresh cilantro leaves if desired. Serve with baked tortilla chips.

NUTRITIONAL VALUE PER SERVING			
Calories	45	Total Fat	0g
Carbohydrates	8g	Saturated Fat	0g
Protein	3g	Cholesterol	0mg
Fiber	3g	Sodium	200mg

Exchanges: 1/2 carbohydrate
Carb Choices: 1/2

shrimp and spring-onion mousse

This flavorful dip can also be spread on homemade pita chips and topped with chopped chives for an easy hors d'oeuvre

Serves: 4

Prep Time: 6 minutes

Chilling Time: 30 minutes

INGREDIENTS

½ cup cooked shrimp (thaw if frozen)

4 ounces (about ½ cup) fat-free cream cheese

1 teaspoon soy sauce

1 teaspoon lemon juice

½ teaspoon your favorite hot sauce

1 tablespoon green onion, chopped (green part only)

1. In a blender or food processor, **PULSE** the shrimp and cream cheese to break up the shrimp.

2. ADD the soy sauce, lemon juice, and hot sauce. Puree until fairly smooth. Add the chopped green onion and puree until smooth.

3. CHILL at least 30 minutes. Serve with low-fat crackers or pita chips.

NUTRITIONAL VALUE PER SERVING			
Calories	60	Total Fat	1g
Carbohydrates	2g	Saturated Fat	0g
Protein	10g	Cholesterol	45mg
Fiber	0g	Sodium	300mg

Exchanges: 1 1/2 very lean meats
Carb Choices: 0

what do I do now?

How do I cook raw shrimp?

You can certainly boil your own shrimp for this dish. Since you are going to puree the shrimp, it's fine to use small- or medium-sized ones. Peel the shrimp. Experts say you don't need to remove the vein in small- or medium-sized shrimp.

COMBINE 6 cups of water, half a lemon, half a small onion, $1/2$ teaspoon of salt, a bay leaf, and a few black peppercorns, and bring to a boil. **BOIL** for 5 minutes. Add the peeled shrimp and cook about 3 minutes until the shrimp are curled and opaque. Remove one shrimp carefully with a slotted spoon and check for doneness. The shrimp is fully cooked when it's pink and opaque. Carefully **DRAIN** the cooked shrimp in a colander and immediately run them under cold running water to stop the cooking process. Keep the shrimp refrigerated until ready to use.

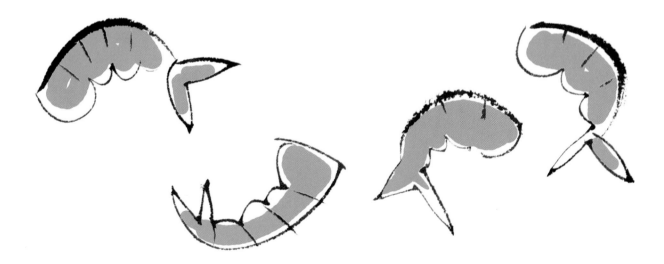

baked zucchini sticks

Crunchy and delicious—with none of the fat of the traditional fried version

Serves: 4

Prep Time: 15 minutes

Cooking Time: 20 minutes

INGREDIENTS

Cooking spray

1 large zucchini

2 egg whites

1/4 cup water

1/4 cup all-purpose flour

1 teaspoon oregano

1 teaspoon salt

1/2 cup bread crumbs

Marinara sauce (optional)

1. **PREHEAT** oven to 375°F. Lightly coat a cookie sheet with cooking spray and set aside.

2. With a vegetable peeler, peel the zucchini. **CUT** the zucchini into 3 sections, then slice each lengthwise into thirds. **CUT** each slice into thirds again to create 27 zucchini sticks.

3. In a small bowl, **WHISK** the egg whites and water. In a separate bowl, mix the flour, 1/2 teaspoon of oregano and 1/2 teaspoon of salt. In a third bowl, mix the bread crumbs with the remaining oregano and salt.

4. Working in batches, toss a few zucchini sticks in the flour mixture; then dip in the egg wash; then **COAT** with the bread crumbs. Arrange the coated zucchini sticks on the prepared cookie sheet. **REPEAT** with the remaining zucchini.

5. **BAKE** 10 minutes. Flip the zucchini sticks. **BAKE** 10 minutes longer until the coating is golden and crisp and the zucchini is cooked but not soggy. Serve with warm marinara sauce if desired.

NUTRITIONAL VALUE PER SERVING			
Calories	100	Total Fat	1g
Carbohydrates	19g	Saturated Fat	0g
Protein	5g	Cholesterol	0mg
Fiber	2g	Sodium	730mg

Exchanges: 1 carbohydrate, 1 vegetable
Carb Choices: 1 1/2

When summer zucchini abounds, make these delicious baked sticks.
Their crunchy coating makes this an appealing appetizer
for everyone, children included.

basic hummus

Hummus, with its low GI index, makes a healthy, delicious snack with crudités or as a sandwich

Serves: 4

Prep Time: 10 minutes

Chilling Time: 60 minutes

INGREDIENTS

1 15-ounce can chickpeas, drained

4 cloves garlic

3 tablespoons olive oil

2 tablespoons tahini (sesame paste)

2 tablespoons lemon juice

2 tablespoons water

$1/4$ teaspoon salt

$1/8$ teaspoon black pepper

1. In a blender or food processor, **PUREE** all ingredients. Blend until smooth. Taste and adjust the salt and pepper as needed.

2. CHILL 1 hour before serving. Optional garnish idea: sprinkle with paprika (about $1/4$ teaspoon will do) and drizzle with a splash of olive oil if desired.

NUTRITIONAL VALUE PER SERVING			
Calories	240	Total Fat	15g
Carbohydrates	23g	Saturated Fat	2g
Protein	6g	Cholesterol	0mg
Fiber	4g	Sodium	400mg

Exchanges: 1 1/2 carbohydrates, 1/2 very lean meat, 3 fats
Carb Choices: 1 1/2

what do I do now?

I don't have any tahini. Are there appropriate substitutions?
There are some hummus recipes that call for peanut butter instead of
tahini. The result is a nuttier-tasting dip. If you substitute peanut
butter for tahini in this recipe, reduce the amount to 1 tablespoon.
Reduce the garlic to one clove and omit the lemon juice.

HUMMUS: A GREAT DIABETIC SNACK

Hummus is made from chickpeas (a.k.a. garbanzo beans) which are a terrific
source of carbohydrates, protein, and fiber. Studies have shown chickpeas
and other legumes (dried beans and peas) to break down slowly in the body,
providing energy without creating uncomfortable spikes in the blood sugar
like other carbohydrates, such as white bread, can. Furthermore, hummus is
quite low in fat, olive oil being the only source. Many of our favorite dips
contain sour cream, cream cheese, or other sources of fat that do little for us
nutritionally. Hummus is smooth and creamy and can be eaten on whole-
wheat crackers, pita chips, or fresh cut veggies. In addition, it can be dolled
up with other spices like cayenne, cumin, chili powder, roasted red peppers,
and a host of other flavorings to give it additional zip.

---

roasted eggplant dip

A smooth, rich dip with the robust flavors of the Middle East

Serves: 6

Prep Time: 10 minutes

Cooking Time: 30-40 minutes

INGREDIENTS

1 medium eggplant

2 teaspoons olive oil

1/2 teaspoon salt

3 cloves garlic

1/4 cup low-sodium chicken broth

1 tablespoon tahini (sesame paste)

1 tablespoon lemon juice

1. **PREHEAT** oven to 350°F.

2. **CUT** eggplant in half lengthwise. Coat a baking sheet and the eggplant halves with 1 teaspoon of olive oil. Sprinkle the cut sides of the eggplant with salt. Roast eggplant, cut sides down, 30 to 40 minutes, until it is very soft and cooked through. **COOL** the eggplant a few minutes before handling.

3. With a large spoon, **SCOOP** the eggplant flesh out of its peel. You should have about 1 cup of cooked eggplant. Discard the peel and any liquid that might have collected in the roasting pan. In a blender or food processor, **PUREE** the eggplant with all the remaining ingredients until smooth. Adjust the salt if necessary. Serve with pita chips or crudités.

NUTRITIONAL VALUE PER SERVING			
Calories	50	Total Fat	3g
Carbohydrates	6g	Saturated Fat	0g
Protein	1g	Cholesterol	0mg
Fiber	2g	Sodium	200mg

Exchanges: 1 vegetable, 1/2 fat
Carb Choices: 1/2

Roasted eggplant adds a delicious, robust flavor to this low-fat dip.

Chapter 4

Soups and Stews

Nothing says comfort as much as a hearty soup. Why not make sure it is good for the heart, too! Here are two healthy soups and stews: Quick Cassoulet (top) and Sweet Potato, Sausage, and Sage Soup (right).

hearty burgundy beef stew

A luscious stew to satisfy big appetites
on chilly days

Serves: 4

Prep Time: 15 minutes

Cooking Time: 20 minutes

Oven Time: 2 hours

INGREDIENTS

1½ pounds rump, chuck, or round roast, trimmed and cubed (1-inch square)

4 teaspoons olive oil

1 medium onion, diced

1 rib of celery, diced

1 medium carrot, peeled and sliced thin

2 cloves garlic, minced

1 cup dry red wine

1 15-ounce can low-sodium beef broth

1 cup water

1 tablespoon Worcestershire sauce

2 teaspoons thyme

½ pound small fresh mushrooms

2 tablespoons cornstarch plus 2 tablespoons water, mixed together

½ teaspoon salt

½ teaspoon black pepper

1. **PREHEAT** oven to 325°F. In a Dutch oven or other heavy, oven-safe pot with a lid, **HEAT** 2 teaspoons olive oil over medium-high heat until very hot. Working in batches, brown the meat on all sides. Adjust heat as needed to avoid burning, but maintain heat so that the meat browns quickly and juices do not collect in the bottom of the pot. Remove the cooked meat and set aside.

2. **ADD** 2 more teaspoons olive oil to the pot. Add onion, celery, and carrot. **COOK** over medium-high heat, stirring often until mixture is softened and browned around the edges. Add the garlic and red wine. Scrape any browned bits from the bottom of the pot.

3. **ADD** the beef broth, water, Worcestershire sauce, and thyme. Return browned beef to the pot. Cover and put in the preheated oven.

4. **CLEAN** mushrooms with a damp paper towel and remove and discard stems.

5. Carefully remove stew from the oven. **ADD** mushrooms and cornstarch mixture. Return pot to the oven and **COOK** 1 hour more. Add salt and black pepper and cook 20 to 30 minutes longer, until the beef can be pierced easily with a fork. Taste, and adjust the salt if necessary.

6. Serve with crusty bread.

Hearty Burgundy stew NUTRITIONAL VALUE PER SERVING			
Calories	400	Total Fat	14g
Carbohydrates	14g	Saturated Fat	4g
Protein	43g	Cholesterol	120mg
Fiber	2g	Sodium	460mg

Exchanges: 2 vegetables, ½ other carbohydrate, 4 ½ lean meat, 1 fat
Carb Choices: 1

what do I do now?

If I don't have rump roast, can I use other cuts of beef?

Tougher cuts of meat or ones that have a higher fat content are best suited to braising (slow cooking in liquid). Good substitutions would be brisket, flank steak, trimmed top, bottom or eye round, and chuck roast.

My oven is already full; can I cook burgundy beef on my stove top?

You can certainly braise on the stove top. However, the indirect, constant heat of the oven will help your beef cook more evenly. You might consider using a crock pot. Brown the meat and vegetables on the stove. You can add the mushrooms in the last hour of cooking.

I'm not familiar with wines, especially for cooking. Can I use a commercially marketed "cooking wine"?

Food experts always say cook with a wine that you'd enjoy drinking. Generally a $6 bottle of burgundy or merlot will do for most dishes calling for red wine. A similarly priced sauvignon blanc will do the trick for recipes calling for white wine.

sweet potato, sausage, and sage soup

Savory sage and sausage balance the sweetness of the potatoes in this rich soup

Serves: 4

Prep Time: 10 minutes

Cooking Time: 35 minutes

INGREDIENTS

4 ounces reduced-fat breakfast sausage

1 cup onion, chopped

1/2 cup celery, chopped

2 medium sweet potatoes, peeled and diced (measuring 3 cups)

2 15-ounce cans low-sodium chicken broth

1 1/2 teaspoons ground sage

1/2 teaspoon paprika

1 cup skim milk

1. In a soup pot over medium-high heat, thoroughly brown the sausage, breaking up the meat into small pieces. Remove the sausage and set aside.

2. ADD onion and celery to the pot. COOK 6 to 8 minutes, stirring often, over medium heat until vegetables are soft and slightly browned on the edges. Add the sweet potatoes and chicken broth. Increase heat to high and bring to a boil. Skim any foam that rises. COOK 10 to 15 minutes, until sweet potatoes can be mashed with a spoon.

3. Working in batches if necessary, PUREE the soup in a blender or food processor. Be careful with the hot liquid. Return the soup to the pot and adjust heat to medium. Add sage and paprika. SIMMER 5 minutes.

4. ADD cooked sausage and milk. HEAT through but do not bring to a rolling boil.

NUTRITIONAL VALUE PER SERVING			
Calories	230	Total Fat	5g
Carbohydrates	33g	Saturated Fat	2g
Protein	13g	Cholesterol	30mg
Fiber	4g	Sodium	350mg
Exchanges: 2 carbohydrates, 1 vegetable, 1 medium-fat meat			
Carb Choices: 2			

This is a rich, creamy, savory soup that can easily be
turned into a main meal: just add a salad and bread.

chicken, corn, and egg drop soup

Sweet corn, tender chicken, and green onion combine perfectly in this deliciously delicate soup

Serves: 4

Prep Time: 10 minutes

Cooking Time: 30 minutes

INGREDIENTS

2 medium boneless skinless chicken breasts (about **10** ounces)

3 cups water

1 teaspoon ground ginger or **1**-inch piece fresh ginger, peeled and diced

1 large clove garlic, minced

1 15-ounce can low-sodium chicken broth

1 15-ounce can low-sodium cream-style corn

1 tablespoon cornstarch plus **1** tablespoon water, mixed together

¹/₈ teaspoon black pepper

2 eggs (or egg whites), beaten

2 bunches green onions, chopped

¹/₄ teaspoon salt

1. **CUT** chicken into 6 chunks and set aside. Bring 2 cups of water to a boil in a covered saucepan. **ADD** the ginger and garlic to the boiling water. Reduce heat to medium and add the chicken. Cover and gently **COOK** the chicken 6 to 8 minutes, until just cooked through. Remove the chicken and rinse off any foam that might be sticking to it. Let cool for a few minutes and then shred the chicken.

2. **HEAT** the chicken broth with the remaining cup of water, cream-style corn, and cornstarch/water mixture. Bring to a boil for 2 minutes. Reduce heat to medium. Add the chicken and black pepper. **SIMMER** 3 minutes.

3. Stir in the beaten eggs. **SIMMER** 3 to 4 minutes longer. **STIR** in the chopped green onions at the last minute of cooking, and salt to taste. Serve hot with sesame crisps or another low-carb cracker.

NUTRITIONAL VALUE PER SERVING			
Calories	240	Total Fat	6g
Carbohydrates	26g	Saturated Fat	2g
Protein	24g	Cholesterol	150mg
Fiber	3g	Sodium	280mg

Exchanges: 1 ¹/₂ carbohydrates, 1 vegetable, 3 very lean meats
Carb Choices: 2

what do I do now?

How do I peel ginger?

A vegetable peeler works quite well. But a regular spoon is a great tool for scraping the thin brown skin off the knobby root. Use a spoon and there's no danger of cutting yourself!

What's the best way to store leftover soup?

As with any leftovers, get them cooled quickly. They should be cooled below room temperature (70°F) within two hours. If you have a large pot of hot soup or stock, set it in a basin filled with iced water. Stir the soup often to lower the temperature at the center of the pot, where temperatures can stay warm enough for bacteria to grow. Store soups in small containers so they can cool more quickly in the fridge or freezer. Don't stack containers of leftovers on top of each other until they are completely cool. Eat refrigerated leftovers within four days. And always bring your leftover soups back to a boil before serving them.

First Person Disaster: *Hold the Salt*

I was making some soup to show off all my new soup bowls. I slowly simmered the vegetables and chicken stock and added the amount of salt called for in the recipe. One hour later, when my soup looked about ready, I tasted it. To my horror, it was way too salty. The recipe had called for sodium-free chicken stock and I had used regular chicken stock. I had to add water to get the salt under control, but, alas, the water diluted the soup's flavor. I wound up adding more vegetables to help absorb the salt. When I told my sister my saga, she said that you should never add salt to a soup or stock until the end of the cooking process. The reason is that the longer a soup cooks, the more its liquid evaporates. With less liquid, less salt is needed.

–Tina B., Asheville, NC

lentil and spinach soup with sausage

Simple flavors come together in this wholesome rustic soup

Serves: 8

Prep Time: 15 minutes

Cooking Time: 40 minutes

INGREDIENTS

6 ounces low-fat smoked sausage, diced into 1/4-inch-thick rounds

2 teaspoons olive oil

3 carrots, peeled and diced (1 cup)

4 stalks celery, diced (1 cup)

1 onion, peeled, and sliced into thin strips lengthwise (1 cup)

1 clove garlic, minced

1 cup lentils, rinsed

3 cups low-sodium chicken broth

3 cups water

1 10-ounce package frozen leaf spinach, thawed (or **4** cups fresh, rinsed well and torn into bits)

1/2-1 teaspoon salt

1/2 teaspoon black pepper

1. **HEAT** 1 teaspoon of olive oil in a soup pot over medium-high heat. Add sausage rounds and brown on all sides. Remove sausage and set aside. Add the remaining olive oil and the carrots, celery, onion, and garlic to the pot. **COOK**, stirring often, until vegetables are soft and slightly browned, about 7 minutes. Add lentils and the chicken broth and water. Bring to a boil, then reduce heat to medium. Cover and cook until lentils are nearly tender but still not completely cooked, about 30 minutes.

2. Remove all liquid from the thawed spinach. **ADD** the spinach to the soup. Cover and **COOK** 10 more minutes, until the lentils are very soft.

3. **ADD** the browned sausage. Add the salt and pepper. Taste and adjust the seasoning. Serve with crusty wheat bread and salad.

NUTRITIONAL VALUE PER SERVING			
Calories	150	Total Fat	2.5g
Carbohydrates	21g	Saturated Fat	0.5g
Protein	12g	Cholesterol	10mg
Fiber	9g	Sodium	560mg

Exchanges: 1 carbohydrate, 2 vegetables, 1 1/2 very lean meats
Carb Choices: 1 1/2

Sausage and spinach turn this lentil soup into a fabulous meal.

golden split-pea soup

Cumin and sautéed onions add robust flavor to this delicious vegetarian soup

Serves: 4

Prep Time: 10 minutes

Cooking Time: 45 minutes

INGREDIENTS

1 cup yellow split peas, picked over

3 cups water

2 teaspoons vegetable oil

1/2 tablespoon cumin

2 onions, chopped

3 cups low-sodium chicken broth

2 bay leaves

2 cloves garlic, minced

1/2 teaspoon black pepper

3/4 teaspoon salt

2 teaspoons dried parsley or **1** tablespoon fresh parsley, minced

1. **COMBINE** split peas and 3 cups water in a medium saucepan. Bring to a boil over medium-high heat, skimming any foam that rises to the surface. **COOK** until split peas begin to break up and become slightly creamy, about 10 minutes.

2. While the split peas cook, **HEAT** the oil in a large separate pot over medium-high heat. Add the cumin and chopped onions and **COOK** 6 to 8 minutes, until the onions are softened and well browned on the edges. Remove from heat and set aside until the split peas have finished cooking.

3. Carefully **ADD** the split peas to the onion mixture. Add 3 cups of chicken broth, the bay leaves, and garlic. Bring to a boil and reduce heat to medium. **COOK** the soup over a low boil for 20 to 25 minutes longer. Add black pepper and salt. **COOK** 5 to 10 minutes longer until flavors have developed fully.

4. The soup should be creamy, with larger pieces of split peas throughout. If you want an even creamier soup, carefully **PUREE** half the soup in a blender and return it to the soup pot. If the soup seems too thick, add one cup of water. Garnish with parsley, and serve with a few pita chips.

NUTRITIONAL VALUE PER SERVING			
Calories	250	Total Fat	3.5g
Carbohydrates	39g	Saturated Fat	1g
Protein	16g	Cholesterol	5mg
Fiber	1g	Sodium	520mg

Exchanges: 2 carbohydrates, 1 vegetable, 2 very lean meats, 1/2 fat
Carb Choices: 2 1/2

what do I do now?

Yellow split peas are high in carbohydrates. Are there any lower carb substitutions?

Many dried legumes (mainly peas and beans) do have a fair amount of carbohydrates. Yellow split peas weigh in at 28 grams of carbohydrates per $1/4$ cup of dried peas. Lentils are lower at about 19 grams of carbohydrates per serving. Red lentils would be a wonderful substitution for yellow split peas, but they are often hard to find in a regular grocery store. When eating legumes, try to limit the other starches in your meal, such as breads and rice. Remember too that legumes contain a lot of dietary fiber, which is important in a healthy diet. Recent studies show that high-fiber foods help keep blood glucose levels in check, so you might consider incorporating them into your diet.

FREEZING FRESH HERBS

You really can't beat the bright flavors of fresh cilantro and parsley in most dishes. Both are found in almost any grocery store and they are the most affordable fresh herbs around. They also freeze remarkably well. Just wash them and place on a towel to dry thoroughly. Remove as much of the stem as possible. You'll probably have to pick the leaves off the cilantro to do this. With a sharp knife on a dry cutting board, hold the leaves in a tight bunch and chop them thinly. After this initial chop, you can run your knife back through the herbs several times for a fine chop. Scoop the herbs into freezer bags. Label them and freeze for up to 2 months. You can also chop the herbs in a food processor, but this often purees them, causing them to freeze in clumps.

French onion soup

Roasting the onions makes
this soup irresistible

Serves: 4

Prep Time: 10 minutes

Cooking Time: 60 minutes

INGREDIENTS

4 medium onions

1 teaspoon olive oil

2 15-ounce cans low-sodium beef broth

4 cups water

1¹/₂ teaspoon Worcestershire sauce

1 tablespoon cornstarch plus 1 tablespoon cold water, mixed

¹/₄ teaspoon black pepper

1 teaspoon dried parsley

¹/₄ teaspoon salt

4 slices low-fat Swiss cheese

4 slices French bread, toasted

1. **PREHEAT** oven to 375°F. Without peeling them, **CUT** 2 onions lengthwise (from the root end to the stem end). Place the onion halves, cut sides down, on a cookie sheet and **BAKE** 30 minutes until soft and browned on the edges.

2. While the onions are baking, peel the remaining two. **CUT** lengthwise (from the root end to the stem end), slice into thin strips, and then chop into small pieces. **HEAT** the olive oil in a large soup pot over medium heat. Add the chopped onions and **COOK** 18 to 20 minutes, stirring often, until the onions are very brown and soft but not burnt. The more care you take with this step, the better.

3. When the oven-roasted onions are cooked, **COOL** slightly before handling. Remove the skin and chop the onions to the same size as the raw onions you chopped earlier. **ADD** the roasted onions to the soup pot. Add the beef broth, water, Worcestershire sauce, cornstarch/water mixture, pepper, parsley and salt. Bring to a boil and **COOK** over medium-high heat 15 minutes, until the flavors have blended. Taste and adjust the seasoning.

4. Lay a slice of cheese over each slice of toasted French bread. **BAKE** on a cookie sheet 5 to 6 minutes, until the cheese has melted. Place a piece of cheesy toast in the bottom of four bowls. **SPOON** hot French onion soup over the toast.

NUTRITIONAL VALUE PER SERVING			
Calories	230	Total Fat	5g
Carbohydrates	30g	Saturated Fat	1.5g
Protein	16g	Cholesterol	10mg
Fiber	3g	Sodium	500mg

Exchanges: 1 carbohydrate, ¹/₂ other carbohydrate, 2 vegetables, 1 lean meat
Carb Choices: 2

what do I do now?

What exactly is caramelizing?

Basically, caramelizing is browning sugar over heat. Not surprisingly, we see caramelization in many dessert recipes. But you often run across caramelization when dealing with onions. The idea is to concentrate the natural sweetness (sugars) and flavor of the onions. You can caramelize onions on the stove with a little oil, sautéing them over a medium heat for 15 to 20 minutes, sometimes longer, stirring often. The onions should soften and begin to brown without sticking or burning. Vegetables can be caramelized in the oven by roasting in the oven at 400-450°F until the vegetables are soft and browned around the edges. Caramelized vegetables add depth of flavor to stews, soups, sauces, and braised or roasted dishes.

quick cassoulet

Inspired by French country fare, this dish takes half the time but has twice the flavor

Serves: 4

Prep Time: 10 minutes

Cooking Time: 40 minutes

INGREDIENTS

4 ounces low-fat, low-sodium smoked sausage

1/2 pound pork tenderloin, silverskin removed (see page 31)

1 tablespoon olive oil

1 small onion, peeled and diced

1 stalk celery, diced

1 carrot, peeled and sliced thin

1 15-ounce can diced tomatoes, drained

2 15-ounce cans cannellini beans, drained and rinsed (navy beans or great northern white beans may be substituted)

1 15-ounce can low-sodium chicken stock

2 cloves garlic, peeled and diced

1 bay leaf

1/2 teaspoon dried thyme

2 teaspoons dried parsley, or **2** tablespoons fresh

Salt and pepper to taste

1. **PREHEAT** oven to 375°F. Slice sausage into 1/4-inch thick slices on a bias. Slice tenderloin into 1/2-inch thick slices.

2. In a large cast-iron skillet or a Dutch oven, **HEAT** the olive oil over high heat until lightly smoking. **SEAR** tenderloin medallions 1 minute on each side. The medallions should have a nice brown crust to them after searing. Remove the medallions from the skillet and set aside. **SEAR** the sausage 30 to 45 seconds on each side. Set the sausage aside.

3. To the same skillet, **ADD** the onion, celery, and carrot. **COOK** 6 to 8 minutes until soft and well browned around the edges. Add the tomatoes, beans, chicken broth, and garlic.

4. **ADD** the bay leaf and thyme. Cover with a suitable pot lid and **SIMMER** for 10 minutes.

5. Remove the bay leaf and discard. Arrange seared sausages and tenderloin medallions over the vegetable and bean mixture. Scatter the parsley over the entire dish. Taste and adjust the salt and pepper. **BAKE** 12 minutes until sauce is bubbling. Serve with crusty bread and a salad.

NUTRITIONAL VALUE PER SERVING			
Calories	330	Total Fat	8g
Carbohydrates	37g	Saturated Fat	2g
Protein	25g	Cholesterol	45mg
Fiber	9g	Sodium	830mg

Exchanges: 2 carbohydrates, 1 1/2 vegetables, 2 1/2 very lean meats, 1 lean meat
Carb Choices: 2 1/2

This hearty French dish is usually made in a Dutch oven—a heavy deep pot
with a tight-fitting domed lid that can be used for stove top cooking or in the oven.
If you don't have a Dutch oven, you can use a casserole with a tight lid
for oven cooking. Just brown your meats and vegetables in a separate pan
on the stove top and transfer them to the casserole.

creamy potato and leek soup

Add a few whole-wheat croutons and a salad
and you have a wonderful winter meal

Serves: 4

Prep Time: 10 minutes

Cooking Time: 45 minutes

INGREDIENTS

1 large leek, white part only

1 tablespoon margarine

3 medium potatoes, peeled and diced (½-inch cubes)

1 bay leaf

3 cups water

1 cube chicken boullion

1 cup whole milk

1 heaping tablespoon fresh parsley, chopped, or 2 teaspoons dried

1 teaspoon pepper

¼ teaspoon salt

1. CLEAN the leek well (see next page) and dice into small pieces.

2. In a medium soup pot over medium-high heat, MELT 1 tablespoon margarine. Add leeks and COOK 6 to 8 minutes, stirring often, until pieces are limp and slightly browned. Do not let the margarine scorch, as this discolors the final soup.

3. ADD the potatoes, bay leaf, and water. Cover and bring to a boil. BOIL 20 to 25 minutes, until the potatoes are soft and can be mashed easily with the back of a spoon.

4. Remove bay leaf. Add the boullion cube. With a potato masher or a large spoon, MASH the potatoes with the cooking liquid. Remove half the potatoes and liquid carefully and PUREE it in a blender or food processor. Return pureed potato mixture to the soup pot. Add the milk, parsley, pepper, and salt. SIMMER over medium-high heat until the soup has thickened and flavors have developed. Taste and adjust the salt and pepper and serve.

NUTRITIONAL VALUE PER SERVING			
Calories	180	Total Fat	5g
Carbohydrates	29g	Saturated Fat	2g
Protein	5g	Cholesterol	10mg
Fiber	3g	Sodium	590mg

Exchanges: 1½ carbohydrates, 1 vegetable, 1 fat
Carb Choices: 2

LEEKS

Leeks look like giant green onions and they are in fact related. But leeks have a milder flavor than onions. Leeks are available in the produce section of most grocery stores. Leeks are wonderful in soups and stews, or sautéed, roasted, or raw in salads. Leeks must be well cleaned before cooking because the tightly layered leaves trap dirt. Usually only the white part of the leek is used, not its rougher green leaves. If you need diced leeks, slit the leek lengthwise several times and hold it under running water before chopping. If you need leek rings, slice the leek, then rinse the slices in a bowl of cold water until all the dirt sinks to the bottom of the bowl.

Chapter 5

Salads & Sandwiches

Here is an easy way to cut down on calories and fat when making salads and sandwiches: just use a sprinkling of cheese and olives and other high-calorie and high-fat flavorings. Here are some delicious examples: Lime Shrimp and Guacamole Sandwich (top) and Light Coleslaw (right).

spinach salad with blue cheese and healthy ranch vinaigrette

Tangy vinaigrette accentuates creamy blue cheese, pecans, and red onions in this flavorful salad

Serves: 4

Prep Time: 7 minutes

INGREDIENTS

6 cups baby spinach, rinsed well and dried

1/2 medium red onion, sliced paper thin

1/4 cup blue cheese, crumbled

4 tablespoons toasted pecan pieces (bacon bits may be substituted)

Salt and pepper to taste

4 tablespoons healthy ranch vinaigrette (see below)

1/3 cup nonfat mayonnaise

HEALTHY RANCH VINAIGRETTE

1/3 cup nonfat sour cream

1/3 cup skim milk

1/2 tablespoon canola oil

1/2 teaspoon garlic powder

1/2 teaspoon onion powder

1/2 teaspoon dill weed

1/2 teaspoon parsley

1 teaspoon black pepper

1 teaspoon white wine vinegar

1/2 teaspoon Dijon mustard

1. **COMBINE** all the ingredients in a large bowl, but reserve two teaspoons of the blue cheese and pecan pieces (or bacon bits) for garnish. Toss well. Taste and adjust the salt and pepper as needed.

2. **TOSS** with healthy ranch vinaigrette. Serve on chilled plates with the reserved blue cheese and pecan pieces (or bacon bits) sprinkled over the top.

HEALTHY RANCH VINAIGRETTE

Serves: 8   Prep Time: 5 minutes

1. **WHISK** all ingredients together.

2. Taste and adjust the seasonings to your preference. **CHILL** and serve.

Makes about 1 cup.

Spinach salad with blue cheese and vinaigrette NUTRITIONAL VALUE PER SERVING			
Calories	110	Total Fat	9g
Carbohydrates	6g	Saturated Fat	2g
Protein	4g	Cholesterol	5mg
Fiber	2g	Sodium	210mg

Exchanges: 1 vegetable, 2 fats
Carb Choices: 1/2

what do I do now?

My salads never taste as good as the ones in a nice restaurant. What should I do?

Good salads are truly works of art. Fine restaurants have an entire department called "pantry" or "garde-manger" that specializes in salads. They've developed a few tricks for good salads:

Fresh ingredients are key. Choose ingredients that complement each other in taste and texture. Try balancing the sourness from a vinaigrette with the sweetness of fruit, the richness of bacon or nuts with the clean bite of a slightly bitter or peppery green.

Dry your greens after washing them. Extra water will dilute your dressing and prevent it from adhering to the leaves, thus encouraging overdressed, soggy, high-calorie salads. A salad spinner works well to dry greens. If you don't have a spinner, try using a clean pillowcase. Shake off the water, then put your wet greens in the case and shake well.

Use a sharp knife when cutting your vegetables. This keeps you from bruising delicate vegetables like tomatoes and mushrooms and makes for better presentation.

How you serve your salad is incredibly important. A little dressing goes a long way if you toss it carefully. Big tongs are fine for serving, but they're too clumsy for tossing. Try using your clean hands to toss your salad. You can use latex gloves if you don't want to get your hands dirty.

Taste your salad, just like any other dish, before serving. A little extra salt and pepper can really make a difference.

Healthy ranch vinaigrette by itself NUTRITIONAL VALUE PER TABLESPOON			
Calories	15	Total Fat	0.5g
Carbohydrates	2g	Saturated Fat	0g
Protein	0g	Cholesterol	0mg
Fiber	0g	Sodium	55mg
Exchanges: 0 Carb Choices: 0			

classic Greek salad with Greek salad dressing

This robust salad looks impressive presented on a platter next to roasted meat or fish

Serves: 4

Prep Time: 7 minutes

INGREDIENTS

4 small ripe tomatoes

1 large cucumber

1 small red onion

1 small green pepper

2-3 cups romaine lettuce, cleaned and thinly sliced

20 olives, pitted, black and/or green

4 tablespoons Greek salad dressing (see below)

GREEK SALAD DRESSING

1 ounce feta cheese, crumbled

1 teaspoon ground garlic

1/4 cup water

2 tablespoons red or white wine vinegar

1/2 teaspoon dried oregano

1/4 teaspoon salt

1/4 teaspoon black pepper

2 tablespoons olive oil

1. **CUT** tomatoes into wedges. **PEEL** stripes down the length of the cucumber. Thinly slice the striped cucumber. Thinly slice the red onion and green pepper.

2. **LAY** a bed of romaine lettuce on a large platter. Arrange the cucumbers in overlapping concentric rings in the middle of the platter. Arrange the tomato wedges around the cucumbers. Lay rings of onion and green pepper over the cucumbers. Scatter the olives over the salad. **POUR** Greek salad dressing evenly over the vegetables. Let sit 5 minutes and serve.

GREEK SALAD DRESSING

Serves: 6   Prep Time: 5 minutes

1. **COMBINE** the feta cheese and all the remaining ingredients, except the olive oil, in a blender. **BLEND** well. Drizzle the olive oil through the top of the blender while the machine is running.

2. Taste and adjust the seasoning as needed and serve.

Makes 1/2 cup.

Classic Greek salad with Greek salad dressing NUTRITIONAL VALUE PER SERVING			
Calories	110	Total Fat	7g
Carbohydrates	12g	Saturated Fat	1.5g
Protein	3g	Cholesterol	5mg
Fiber	4g	Sodium	320mg

Exchanges: 2 1/2 vegetables, 1 1/2 fats
Carb Choices: 1 1/2

When it comes to salads, presentation is key. Array your greens and cut vegetables in a pleasing pattern.

Greek salad dressing by itself NUTRITIONAL VALUE PER TABLESPOON			
Calories	40	Total Fat	4g
Carbohydrates	1g	Saturated Fat	1g
Protein	1g	Cholesterol	5mg
Fiber	0g	Sodium	115mg
Exchanges: 1 fat Carb Choices: 0			

light coleslaw

Crisp and naturally sweet, this is the perfect accompaniment to a sandwich

Serves: 6

Prep Time: 10 minutes

INGREDIENTS

½ medium white cabbage (8 cups or a 16-ounce bag)

1 carrot, peeled and grated (about 1 cup)

⅓ small onion, finely chopped (¼ cup)

⅓ cup plain nonfat yogurt

¼ cup nonfat mayonnaise

1 tablespoon lemon juice

½ teaspoon salt

Pinch of Splenda or other sweetener

1 tablespoon celery seed

1. Remove and discard the core and outer leaves of the cabbage and CHOP fine the remaining leaves. COMBINE the cabbage, carrot, and onion in a medium bowl.

2. In another small bowl, WHISK together the yogurt, mayonnaise, lemon juice, salt, Splenda, and celery seed. POUR over the vegetables and mix. The coleslaw should be lightly dressed, but if the salad looks too dry, add a bit more yogurt and mayonnaise. Refrigerate until serving.

3. ADD salt and serve. If you prefer a sweeter coleslaw, add a bit more Splenda or other sweetener to taste.

This is an easy and nutritious salad that lasts for days. Make a batch to have on hand.

Mama's potato and beet salad

A unique flavor combination, this is a delicious, low-fat addition to any picnic

Serves: 4-6

Prep Time: 15 minutes

Cooking time: 15 minutes

INGREDIENTS

4 thin-skinned, medium white potatoes, peeled

1½ teaspoon salt

1 medium yellow onion

3 eggs, hardboiled

1 15-ounce can whole beets, rinsed and drained

2 tablespoons olive oil

1 tablespoon white vinegar

1 teaspoon black pepper

½-1 packet Equal or **1** tablespoon Splenda

1. **SLICE** peeled potatoes thin, about ¼-inch thick. Cover with cold water and bring to a boil. Reduce heat and **COOK** potatoes over barely boiling water until tender, about 10 to 15 minutes. Drain and sprinkle with 1 teaspoon of salt while they are still warm.

2. While the potatoes are cooking, thinly slice the onion. Sprinkle with ¼ teaspoon salt and let sit 3 minutes. Rinse in a collander under running water and squeeze out any extra moisture.

3. While the potatoes are cooking and the onion is soaking, **PEEL** and thinly **SLICE** the eggs. Slice the beets to the same thickness as the potatoes.

4. In a small bowl **WHISK** together olive oil, vinegar, ¼ teaspoon salt, pepper and Equal. Add the soaked and squeezed onion slices.

5. In a large bowl, **COMBINE** the potatoes, beets, and eggs. Add the onion mixture and gently **MIX**. Your hands, thoroughly washed, are a good tool for this as they are less likely to break the beets and eggs. Taste and adjust the salt and pepper. Serve chilled or at room temperature.

Light coleslaw NUTRITIONAL VALUE PER SERVING			
Calories	50	Total Fat	0.5g
Carbohydrates	11g	Saturated Fat	0g
Protein	2g	Cholesterol	0mg
Fiber	3g	Sodium	310mg

Exchanges: 2 vegetables
Carb Choices: 1

Mama's potato and beet salad NUTRITIONAL VALUE PER SERVING			
Calories	190	Total Fat	7g
Carbohydrates	27g	Saturated Fat	1.5g
Protein	6g	Cholesterol	105mg
Fiber	3g	Sodium	730mg

Exchanges: 1½ carbohydrates, ½ vegetable, ½ medium-fat meat, 1 fat
Carb Choices: 2

oven-fried chicken salad

Crisp, juicy chicken over smooth, buttery lettuce will satisfy the heartiest appetites

Serves: 2

Prep Time: 20 minutes

Cooking Time: 10 minutes

INGREDIENTS

½ cucumber, peeled

2 radishes

1 tablespoon white wine vinegar

½ packet Splenda or Equal

1 large boneless skinless chicken breast or 2 thin chicken cutlets

½ teaspoon salt

½ teaspoon black pepper

1 egg

⅛ cup water

¼ cup bread crumbs

Cooking spray

1 head Boston or bibb lettuce, cut into quarters (chopped romaine can be used for a crunchier salad)

2 tablespoons crumbled blue cheese or grated cheddar (optional)

¼ small red onion, very thinly sliced

4 tablespoons healthy ranch vinaigrette (see page 72)

1. **PREHEAT** oven to 450°F.

2. **SLICE** the cucumber and radishes thinly. Toss with the vinegar and sweetener. Let sit 5 minutes. Remove from the mixture.

3. **LAY** the chicken on a cutting board. Holding the blade of your knife parallel to the cutting board, **SLICE** the chicken breast in half. Beat the egg and water in a bowl. In another bowl mix the bread crumbs with some salt and pepper. Dip the chicken in the egg wash. Shake off the excess and coat with bread crumbs. Lay on a cookie sheet that's been lightly coated with cooking oil spray. Lightly spray the breaded chicken with cooking oil spray. **BAKE** 3 minutes, then carefully flip the chicken. **BAKE** another 2 to 4 minutes, until the chicken is firm and golden. Remove from the oven and let sit 1 minute.

4. **ARRANGE** two wedges of lettuce, cut sides up, in an inverted "V" on each salad plate. Arrange the marinated cucumber and radish slices around the outside of each wedge. **CUT** each piece of chicken in two and overlap them on the top of the lettuce wedges. If desired, sprinkle the cheese over the chicken. Pile the sliced onions on top. Drizzle healthy ranch vinaigrette (see page 72) over the salad and serve immediately.

SAFETY NOTE: Always wash your hands with soap and water after touching raw meats. Prep your salad vegetables with a different knife and cutting board than you use for the chicken. Consider prepping your vegetables and salad dressing before handling the chicken to avoid cross-contamination.

Turn an ordinary chicken salad into a feast of flavors with a tangy cucumber-and-radish relish and a dollop of healthy ranch vinegrette.

Oven-fried chicken salad with healthy ranch vinegrette
NUTRITIONAL VALUE PER SERVING

Calories	260	Total Fat	7g
Carbohydrates	19g	Saturated Fat	2g
Protein	27g	Cholesterol	160mg
Fiber	2g	Sodium	890mg

Exchanges: 1/2 carbohydrate, 2 vegetables, 3 very lean meats, 1/2 medium-fat meat
Carb Choices: 1 1/2

Asian steak salad with Asian soy sesame sauce

Succulent steak tops crisp cabbage to make a tasty supper salad

Serves: 4

Prep Time: 20 minutes

Cooking Time: 10 minutes

Marinating Time: 12-24 hours

INGREDIENTS

12-ounce flank steak (trimmed pork tenderloin may be substituted)

2 teaspoons canola oil

FOR MARINADE

1/2 cup white wine, rice wine, sherry, or vermouth

1/4 cup reduced-sodium soy sauce

3 cloves garlic, chopped

2 tablespoons fresh ginger, chopped

FOR SALAD

1 small napa cabbage or 4 cups romaine lettuce torn into small bits

1 red onion, peeled

1/2 teaspoon salt

4 radishes

1 cucumber

1 cup white mushrooms, sliced

1 carrot, peeled

4 tablespoons Asian soy sesame sauce (see next page)

1. With a sharp knife, PIERCE the flank steak several times (about 10 times) on both sides. Place the steak, 1 teaspoon canola oil, and all marinating ingredients in a sealable plastic bag. MARINATE at least 12 hours. If the steak is too long for the bag, it's fine to cut it in half.

2. PREHEAT the oven to 475°F.

3. Separate the leaves of the cabbage and RINSE under running water. Shake leaves well and place them on a kitchen towel to dry. Stack the cabbage and slice thinly. Thinly SLICE the red onion. Sprinkle with salt and let sit 3 minutes. Rinse well and squeeze out all the water. Thinly slice the radishes, cucumber, and mushrooms. CUT the carrot into thin matchsticks.

4. On a platter, arrange a bed of cabbage. PLACE the cucumbers on top of the cabbage and the carrots on top of the cucumbers (set a few carrots aside for garnish). Lay the mushrooms on top of the carrots.

5. On the stove top, HEAT an oven-safe skillet on high heat. Remove the steak from the marinade and pat dry with a paper towel. Rub the remaining canola oil on all sides. Place the meat in the hot skillet and SEAR for 1 minute. Flip the meat and sear again for 1 minute. The pan will probably smoke. Put the pan in the preheated oven and COOK undisturbed for 5 minutes for medium-rare, 7 minutes for medium. Transfer the meat to a cutting board and let rest 4 minutes. With a sharp knife, slice the meat thinly across the grain. Arrange the meat neatly on top of the bed of vegetables. Arrange the onions, radish slices, and reserved carrot sticks over the meat. Pour the Asian soy sesame dressing (see next page) over the entire salad and serve.

NAPA CABBAGE

Napa cabbage is sometimes called Chinese cabbage, but it should not be confused with bok choy, another Chinese cabbage. Napa is light green and white. It comes in tightly packed, oblong heads. It's wonderful raw, in soups or in stir-fry. When using it raw, peel away any limp outer layers that may be surrounding the crisp inner ones.

ASIAN SOY SESAME SAUCE

Serves: 4   Cooking Time: 5 minutes

1 large clove garlic, peeled

2 teaspoons Splenda

2 tablespoons low-sodium soy sauce

2 tablespoons rice wine vinegar

2 tablespoons water

1 teaspoon sesame oil or canola oil

I. CHOP the garlic into tiny pieces. Using a mortar and pestle, or in a small bowl with the back of a spoon, **CRUSH** the garlic with the sweetener to release the oils in the garlic.

2. ADD the remaining ingredients, mix well, and serve.

Makes about ¼ cup.

Asian steak salad with Asian soy sesame sauce NUTRITIONAL VALUE PER SERVING			
Calories	210	Total Fat	10g
Carbohydrates	9g	Saturated Fat	3g
Protein	20g	Cholesterol	45mg
Fiber	3g	Sodium	960mg
Exchanges: 2 vegetables, 2½ lean meats Carb Choices: ½			

Asian soy sesame sauce by itself NUTRITIONAL VALUE PER TABLESPOON			
Calories	15	Total Fat	1g
Carbohydrates	1g	Saturated Fat	0g
Protein	0g	Cholesterol	0mg
Fiber	0g	Sodium	450mg
Exchanges: 0 Carb Choices: 0			

lime shrimp and guacamole sandwich

The delicate sweetness of shrimp and avocado, with a zip of fresh lime, makes for a simply delicious sandwich

Serves: 4

Prep Time: 10 minutes

INGREDIENTS

2 cups cooked shrimp

3 teaspoons lime juice

1 ripe avocado, mashed

1/2 cup cucumber, chopped

1/2 cup tomato, chopped

2 tablespoons onion, minced

Pinch of salt

Pinch of black pepper

8 slices light wheat bread, toasted

8 Boston or bibb lettuce leaves, washed and dried

1. In a small bowl, MIX the shrimp and 2 teaspoons of lime juice, and set aside. In a separate bowl, mix the avocado and 1 teaspoon of lime juice. In another bowl, mix the cucumber, tomato, onion, salt, and black pepper.

2. SPREAD the avocado mixture on 4 slices of toast. SPOON the tomato mixture on top of the avocado. Arrange shrimp over the tomato and avocado. TOP each with 2 lettuce leaves and another slice of toast. Press down on each sandwich to secure and serve immediately.

what is it and where do I get it?

COOKED SHRIMP

Frozen salad shrimp work just great for sandwich-filling, and they're readily available in the frozen fish section of your grocery store. While not the best option, canned shrimp would work in pinch. You could always cook your own. See tips on cooking shrimp on page 45.

Lime shrimp and guacamole sandwich
NUTRITIONAL VALUE PER SERVING

Calories	240	Total Fat	9g
Carbohydrates	25g	Saturated Fat	1.5g
Protein	18g	Cholesterol	110mg
Fiber	6g	Sodium	360mg

Exchanges: 1 1/2 carbohydrates, 1/2 vegetable, 2 very lean meats, 1 1/2 fats
Carb Choices: 1 1/2

Bring the art of "spa" cooking to your luncheon table with this flavorful,
elegant Lime Shrimp and Guacamole Sandwich served on low-carbohydrate wheat bread. While any lettuce will do,
try Boston or Bibb lettuce. Their greens are sweet and tender.

down-home turkey sandwich

No need to wait for Thanksgiving
to enjoy this savory turkey feast

Serves: 1-2

Prep Time: 8 minutes

Cooking Time: 20 minutes

INGREDIENTS

1 teaspoon olive oil

1 small onion, thinly sliced

½ tablespoon nonfat mayonnaise

2-4 slices light wheat bread, toasted

2-4 ounces low-sodium deli turkey, thinly sliced

2 tablespoons cranberry sauce (look for a brand that is low in sugar)

I. HEAT the olive oil over medium heat in a small nonstick pan. Add the onion and **COOK** until soft, brown and well caramelized, about 20 minutes.

2. SPREAD the mayonnaise on each piece of toast. Lay the caramelized onions on one slice of toast. **TOP** with folded slices of turkey and cranberry sauce. Top with another slice of toast. Serve with a salad or vegetable crudités (see page 39).

NUTRITIONAL VALUE PER SERVING

Calories	190	Total Fat	3g
Carbohydrates	29g	Saturated Fat	0.5g
Protein	15g	Cholesterol	25mg
Fiber	4g	Sodium	580mg

Exchanges: 1½ carbohydrates, ½ other carbohydrate, 2 very lean meats, ½ fat
Carb Choices: 2

dilly egg salad sandwich

Aromatic dill and fewer yolks bring a
fresh twist to this old favorite

Serves: 4

Prep Time: 10 minutes

Cooking Time: 20 minutes

INGREDIENTS

7 large eggs

1/2 stalk of celery,
diced small

1/2 small red onion,
diced small

1/4 cup nonfat
mayonnaise

2 teaspoons dried dill
weed, or **1 1/2** tablespoons
fresh dill

2 teaspoons white wine
vinegar or lemon juice

1/2 teaspoon Dijon
mustard

1/4 teaspoon salt

1/4 teaspoon black pepper

8 slices light wheat or
sourdough bread

1. PLACE the eggs in a saucepan. Cover with cold water. Bring to a boil. As soon as the water boils, turn off the heat and cover the pan with a lid. Let stand 15 minutes for hard-boiled eggs. Drain and peel the eggs and rinse under cold water immediately. **CUT** 3 of the eggs in half. Discard the yolks. In a small bowl, **CHOP** or **GRATE** the cooked egg whites and 4 peeled boiled eggs. Add the celery and onion.

2. In a small bowl, **COMBINE** the mayonnaise, dill, vinegar or lemon juice, mustard, salt, and black pepper. **POUR** the mayonnaise mixture over the eggs, celery, and onion. Mix well. Add salt and pepper. (Adjust with additional salt and pepper if necessary.) Refrigerate until ready to serve.

3. ASSEMBLE the sandwiches on slices of wheat or sourdough bread.

NUTRITIONAL VALUE PER SERVING			
Calories	200	Total Fat	7g
Carbohydrates	24g	Saturated Fat	2g
Protein	14g	Cholesterol	215mg
Fiber	4g	Sodium	590mg

Exchanges: 1 1/2 other carbohydrates, 1/2 very lean meat,
1 medium-fat meat
Carb Choices: 1 1/2

Chapter 6

Meats

Ah, the main course. Here are a few easy-to-make entrees that are as healthy as they are delicious. There's Steak Roulade (top) and Stir-Baked Beef and Green Beans (right).

quick kibbe with yogurt dressing

Middle Eastern meatballs traditionally made with bulgur wheat use bran instead in this version

Serves: 4-6

Prep Time: 10 minutes

Cooking Time: 25 minutes

INGREDIENTS

1/2 cup All-Bran cereal

1/4-1/3 cup water

1 pound lean ground beef

2 cloves garlic, grated

1 medium onion, grated

1/2 teaspoon ground ginger or 1 teaspoon fresh ginger, grated

1 teaspoon ground cumin

1 teaspoon ground cinnamon

1/2 teaspoon salt

1/4 teaspoon black pepper

1 1/4 cups yogurt dressing (see below)

YOGURT DRESSING

1 cucumber

1 clove garlic, grated

1/4 cup plain yogurt

1 tablespoon fresh mint, chopped (optional)

1/4 teaspoon ground cumin

1/2 teaspoon salt

1. PREHEAT oven to 425°F. **COMBINE** All-Bran cereal and water and let sit until the cereal is very soft. Combine the cereal mixture with the remaining ingredients and mix very well. **TEST** the seasoning by cooking a small patty and tasting it. Adjust the seasoning if needed.

2. FORM 12 football-shaped meatballs. Arrange the meatballs on a baking sheet. **BAKE** 20 to 25 minutes, until the meatballs are firm and cooked through. Serve with yogurt dressing, pita bread, or couscous.

YOGURT DRESSING

Serves: 4   Prep Time: 7 minutes

1. PEEL the cucumber in stripes. **CUT** the cucumber lengthwise and remove the seeds with a spoon. Grate the cucumber on a box grater. Squeeze out the extra liquid from the grated cucumber.

2. COMBINE the cucumber, garlic, yogurt, mint, and cumin in a bowl. Mix well. Taste and adjust the salt to your preference. **CHILL** and serve. Makes 1 1/4 cups.

Quick kibbe with yogurt dressing
NUTRITIONAL VALUE PER SERVING

Calories	150	Total Fat	7g
Carbohydrates	6g	Saturated Fat	3g
Protein	17g	Cholesterol	30mg
Fiber	2g	Sodium	260mg

Exchanges: 1/2 carbohydrate, 2 lean meats
Carb Choices: 1/2

what do I do now?

How much meat should I cook per person?

The American Diabetes Association considers 3 ounces of cooked, lean meat to be one portion. That's the size of a deck of playing cards. When portioning raw meat for cooking, be aware that meat does shrink a bit during cooking, generally by about a quarter of its raw weight. Cooking 4 ounces of raw lean meat will yield a 3-ounce portion. Conveniently, 1 pound of raw, boneless meat will usually yield four 3-ounce portions.

What's the best way to freeze meat?

Freezing portions makes good sense, just make sure your freezer is set as close to 0°F as possible. This will help the meat freeze quickly, keeping large ice crystals from forming on the meat. Also make sure to wrap meat well in plastic wrap or wax paper before storing it in a freezer bag. Pork chops and roasts should be eaten within 4 to 6 months after freezing. Beef roasts and steaks can be kept 6 to 12 months if properly wrapped. Ground meats should be used within 3 to 4 months of freezing. And remember, meat should be thawed in the refrigerator, in a watertight bag under cold water or in a microwave. Meat should never be left to thaw on a counter at room temperature.

Yogurt dressing by itself NUTRITIONAL VALUE PER TABLESPOON			
Calories	5	Total Fat	0g
Carbohydrates	1g	Saturated Fat	0g
Protein	0g	Cholesterol	0mg
Fiber	0g	Sodium	60mg
Exchanges: 0 Carb Choices: 0			

easy Carolina barbecue

Braising lean pork tenderloin saves time and calories in our take on southern pig pickin'

Serves: 6-8

Prep Time: 10 minutes

Cooking Time: 1-1½ hours

Marinating Time: 30 minutes

INGREDIENTS

2 pounds pork tenderloin (pork loin may be substituted)

1 teaspoon canola oil

3 garlic cloves

2 bay leaves

1 15-ounce can low-sodium chicken stock

3-4 cups water

4 tablespoons spicy barbecue sauce (see below)

SPICY BARBECUE SAUCE

1 cup braising liquid

½ cup white vinegar

2 tablespoons Splenda

½ teaspoon cornstarch

½-1 teaspoon red pepper flakes

¼ teaspoon black pepper

Pinch of salt

1. **PREHEAT** the oven to 325°F. **TRIM** fat and silverskin from the pork (see page 31).

2. Heat a Dutch oven or a heavy skillet over medium-high heat with the oil. Add the pork and **SEAR** on all sides until richly browned. If you're using a Dutch oven, just add the garlic, bay leaves, broth, and enough water to reach halfway up the pork. If you aren't using a Dutch oven, transfer the meat to a casserole dish with a tight-fitting lid. **ADD** the garlic, bay leaves, broth, and enough water to reach halfway up the pork. Place in the oven and **COOK** undisturbed for 1 to 1½ hours until a meat thermometer inserted into the thickest part of the meat reads 160°F.

3. Let the pork cool. Save the braising liquid to make spicy barbecue sauce (see below). **SHRED** the pork with your fingers and set aside.

4. When ready to eat, **WARM** the shredded pork in a skillet on the stovetop or covered in the microwave. Serve the shredded pork with the spicy barbecue sauce spooned over the top. It is delicious on its own or in sandwiches, enchiladas, and other dishes.

SPICY BARBECUE SAUCE

Serves: 4   Prep Time: 5 minutes

1. **HEAT** the reserved braising liquid, vinegar, Splenda, and cornstarch over medium-high heat until the sauce thickens slightly.

2. **ADD** the red pepper flakes and black pepper. **SIMMER**. Taste and adjust the sweetness and saltiness, and serve over shredded pork.

Makes 1½ cups.

what is it and where do I get it?

LEAN MEAT

Lean meats are readily available in any grocery store. But what does lean really mean? The U.S. Department of Agriculture considers meat (beef, pork, or poultry) "lean" if it contains less than 10 grams of fat per 3-ounce serving. "Extra lean" contains less than 5 grams of fat per 3-ounce serving. If the nutrition information is not printed directly on the meat package, a rule of thumb is to look for cuts that have "loin" or "round" in the name. Top round, eye of round, round tip, sirloin, tenderloin, top loin, and flank steak are good lean choices for beef. For pork, rib chops and boneless rib roasts are the lean choices. Skinless chicken breast is the leanest cut of poultry (see page 119).

Easy Carolina barbecue with spicy sauce NUTRITIONAL VALUE PER SERVING			
Calories	160	Total Fat	5g
Carbohydrates	1g	Saturated Fat	1.5g
Protein	25g	Cholesterol	70mg
Fiber	0g	Sodium	80mg
Exchanges: 3 lean meats Carb Choices: 0			

Spicy barbecue sauce by itself NUTRITIONAL VALUE PER TABLESPOON			
Calories	5	Total Fat	0g
Carbohydrates	1g	Saturated Fat	0g
Protein	0g	Cholesterol	0mg
Fiber	0g	Sodium	5mg
Exchanges: 0 Carb Choices: 0			

Chinese meatballs with Asian soy sesame sauce

These meatballs are delicious served with brown rice and garlicky mustard greens

Serves: 4

Prep Time: 15 minutes

Cooking Time: 20-30 minutes

INGREDIENTS

4 cups napa cabbage (see page 81) or **3** cups white cabbage, tough parts removed, chopped

$1/2$ teaspoon salt

1 pound lean ground beef

4 green onions, chopped

3 cloves garlic, minced

1 tablespoon cornstarch

1 tablespoon low-sodium soy sauce

1 teaspoon ground ginger

$1/4$ teaspoon black pepper

Cooking spray

4 tablespoons Asian Soy Sesame Sauce (see below)

ASIAN SOY SESAME SAUCE

1 large clove garlic, peeled

2 teaspoons Splenda

2 tablespoons low-sodium soy sauce

2 tablespoons rice wine vinegar

2 tablespoons water

1 teaspoon sesame oil

1. SPRINKLE the cabbage with salt and toss. Let sit 5 minutes to release its water. Rinse and squeeze out as much moisture as possible. COMBINE the cabbage with all the remaining ingredients, except the Asian Soy Sesame Sauce. Test the seasoning by cooking a small patty in a frying pan. Adjust the seasoning if necessary.

2. SHAPE 12 meatballs. Arrange the meatballs on a baking sheet coated with cooking spray. BAKE in a preheated 400°F oven for 20 to 25 minutes. Serve with Asian Soy Sesame Sauce spooned over the top. Serve with brown rice and Garlicky Mustard Greens (see page 167).

ASIAN SOY SESAME SAUCE

Serves: 4   Prep Time: 5 minutes

1. CHOP the garlic into tiny pieces. Using a mortar and pestle or in a small bowl using the back of a spoon, CRUSH the garlic with the sweetener to release the oils in the garlic.

2. ADD the remaining ingredients, mix well, and serve.

Makes about $1/2$ cup.

See page 81 for Asian Soy Sesame Sauce nutritional value information.

Chinese meatballs with Asian soy sesame sauce NUTRITIONAL VALUE PER SERVING			
Calories	240	Total Fat	12g
Carbohydrates	8g	Saturated Fat	4.5g
Protein	25g	Cholesterol	40mg
Fiber	2g	Sodium	920mg

Exchanges: 1 vegetable, 3 lean meats
Carb Choices: 1/2

peachy braised ham steak

Succulent ham gently cooked in a sweet peach glaze is the ultimate in comfort food

Serves: 4

Prep Time: 6 minutes

Cooking Time: 25 minutes

Soaking Time: 1-2 hours

INGREDIENTS

1 pound ham steak

Cooking spray

1 shallot, chopped

1 can sliced peaches or apricot halves, packed in juice (not syrup)

1 tablespoon peach or apricot fruit spread

1½ teaspoons cornstarch

1 cup low-sodium chicken broth or water

½ teaspoon ground ginger

1. TRIM the fat from the ham. Cut the ham into 4 equal pieces, then rinse it under running water. Place the ham in a large bowl and cover with cold water. Soak the ham for 1 to 2 hours in the refrigerator to remove extra salt.

2. HEAT a medium skillet over medium heat and coat with cooking spray. Add the shallot and **COOK** until softened, about 2 minutes. Drain the canned fruit, reserving the juice for later. Add the fruit to the pan and brown on both sides. Add the fruit spread and cook another minute. **DISSOLVE** the cornstarch in the broth and add to the pan. Add the reserved fruit juice and ginger to the pan.

3. Dry the ham pieces on paper towels and place in the peach braising liquid. **SIMMER** uncovered 20 minutes, turning occasionally until the ham is firm and cooked through. **ADD** a little water or broth if the sauce begins to get too thick, and serve.

NUTRITIONAL VALUE PER SERVING			
Calories	210	Total Fat	5g
Carbohydrates	18g	Saturated Fat	2g
Protein	24g	Cholesterol	50mg
Fiber	2g	Sodium	735mg

Exchanges: 1 fruit, 3 lean meats
Carb Choices: 1

rosemary roast pork tenderloin

*This simple method for cooking
makes lean pork fragrant and juicy*

Serves: 4

Prep Time: 6 minutes

Cooking Time: 15 minutes

Marinating Time: 30 minutes

INGREDIENTS

1 pound pork tenderloin

3 cloves garlic, peeled and chopped

1/2 cup dry white wine

4 3-inch sprigs fresh rosemary or **2** tablespoons dried rosemary

1 teaspoon salt

1 teaspoon olive oil

1 teaspoon cracked black pepper

1. TRIM tenderloin and remove silverskin (see page 31). COMBINE tenderloin, garlic, wine, rosemary, and 1/2 teaspoon salt in a sealable plastic bag and marinate at room temperature for 30 minutes.

2. PREHEAT the oven to 450°F.

3. Dry the tenderloin on paper towels. Rub with the olive oil, 1/2 teaspoon salt, and black pepper. HEAT an oven-safe skillet over medium-high heat. Add the tenderloin and sear 30 seconds on all sides. Immediately transfer the skillet to the oven. ROAST 6 minutes for medium and 8 minutes for well done. Let the pork rest 5 minutes before cutting. Serve with sweet potato mash (see page 160).

what do I do now?

How much meat should I cook per person?
The American Diabetes Association considers 3 ounces of cooked, lean meat to be one portion. That's the size of a deck of playing cards. When portioning raw meat for cooking, be aware that meat does shrink a bit during cooking, generally by about a quarter of its raw weight. Cooking 4 ounces of raw lean meat will yield a 3-ounce portion. Conveniently, 1 pound of raw, boneless meat will usually yield four 3-ounce portions.

NUTRITIONAL VALUE PER SERVING			
Calories	190	Total Fat	6g
Carbohydrates	3g	Saturated Fat	1.5g
Protein	24g	Cholesterol	65mg
Fiber	2g	Sodium	630mg

Exchanges: 3 lean meats
Carb Choices: 0

light beef stroganoff

*Hearty beef and chunky mushrooms mingle
in a luscious but light creamy sauce*

Serves: 4-6

Prep Time: 10 minutes

Cooking Time: 25 minutes

INGREDIENTS

1 pound sirloin steak, sliced into 1- to 2-inch long pieces 1/4-inch thick

2 teaspoons Worcestershire sauce

1/2 teaspoon salt

1/2 teaspoon black pepper

Cooking spray

1/2 pound button mushrooms

1/2 medium onion, chopped

1 tablespoon flour

1 15-ounce can low-sodium beef broth

1/2 cup low-fat milk

1/2 cup nonfat sour cream

4 cups cooked egg noodles

1. Lightly SEASON the beef with 1 teaspoon Worcestershire sauce, salt, and 1/4 teaspoon black pepper. HEAT a heavy skillet over medium-high heat. Coat with cooking spray. Add the beef. Let the beef sizzle a few seconds to get it nicely browned before stirring. BROWN the beef quickly. Remove it from the pan after approximately 2 minutes and set aside. The meat should not be cooked through.

2. While the beef is cooking, coarsely CHOP the mushrooms and stems and set both aside.

3. Add a little more cooking spray to the skillet if necessary. Add the onion and COOK until soft and translucent, about 2 minutes. Add all the mushrooms and cook until they begin to release moisture and start to brown at the edges, about 5 minutes. Add the flour. STIR to coat the vegetables.

4. ADD the broth and scrape up any browned bits in the skillet. Bring to a boil, then reduce heat and SIMMER 6 to 8 minutes, until the sauce thickens slightly.

5. WHISK the milk and sour cream together. POUR it gently into the simmering sauce. To avoid a "curdled" appearance, do not boil the sauce after the cream has been added. Add the remaining Worcestershire sauce and black pepper. SIMMER 10 minutes until the sauce has thickened and flavors have come together.

6. Return the beef and any meat juices that have collected to the pan. SIMMER 5 to 8 minutes, until the meat is completely cooked through. Taste and adjust the salt and pepper. Serve immediately over egg noodles.

NUTRITIONAL VALUE PER SERVING			
Calories	320	Total Fat	9g
Carbohydrates	34g	Saturated Fat	3.5g
Protein	25g	Cholesterol	80mg
Fiber	2g	Sodium	320mg

Exchanges: 2 carbohydrates, 2 lean meats, 1 fat
Carb Choices: 2 1/2

easy oven fajitas

Sizzling beef, onions, and peppers in a corn tortilla make for a zesty meal

Serves: 4

Prep Time: 20 minutes

Cooking Time: 15 minutes

Marinating Time: 30 minutes

INGREDIENTS

3/4 pound skirt steak

2 tablespoons low-sodium soy sauce

3-4 tablespoons lime juice

1 large yellow onion, peeled

1 green pepper

1/2 red pepper

1 teaspoon canola oil

1 tablespoon cilantro, chopped or **1** teaspoon dried cilantro

12 4-inch corn tortillas

1. **SLICE** the steak into thin, 2-inch-long strips, across the grain. **COMBINE** with the soy sauce and lime juice, reserving a dash of lime juice for the finished dish. **MARINATE** at room temperature for 30 minutes.

2. While the steak strips marinate, **PREHEAT** the oven to 475°F. Cut the onion and peppers into thin strips and place in a bowl. Remove the steak from the marinade and dry the steak with paper towels. **TOSS** the steak with 1/2 teaspoon canola oil. Place an oven-safe skillet on a hot stove for one minute. Add the steak to the hot skillet and cook 2 minutes.

3. In a bowl, toss the vegetables and cilantro with 1/2 teaspoon oil. **ADD** the vegetables to the steak in the hot skillet and stir quickly, then place in oven. **ROAST** 7 minutes or until the vegetables are crisp and slightly browned at the edges. Taste and adjust the seasoning if desired. Squeeze some lime juice over the finished dish. Serve with warmed corn tortillas and garnish with nonfat sour cream, chopped tomato, or chopped red onion, if desired.

NUTRITIONAL VALUE PER SERVING			
Calories	270	Total Fat	9g
Carbohydrates	25g	Saturated Fat	3g
Protein	22g	Cholesterol	45mg
Fiber	2g	Sodium	570mg

Exchanges: 1 1/2 carbohydrates, 1 vegetable, 2 lean meats
Carb Choices: 1 1/2

what do I do now?

What does it mean to cut meat "across the grain" and why should I do it?

All meat is made of bundles of long muscle fibers held together by connective protein tissue. If you look closely at a piece of meat, particularly flank steak or a roast, you'll notice little horizontal lines in it. These are the connective tissues and the bundles of muscle fiber. Cutting across the grain means cutting across these muscle bundles. Cutting thin slices across the grain makes meat easier to chew. Leaner and seemingly tougher cuts can be made tender after slicing in this manner.

I find lean meat rather tough after it's cooked. Can I tenderize it?

Absolutely! Marinating is one popular method of tenderizing. Marinades typically contain an acid, such as vinegar, wine, or citrus juice, that breaks down proteins in the meat. Some plant enzymes, such as those in papaya, pineapple, and some mushrooms, will do the same thing. Of course these will affect the flavor of the meat. And these acids and enzymes can cause the meat to lose more of its natural moisture when cooked.

Slow, moist heat, as with braising, is a good way to make a large lean round or rump roast come out tender. But beware of overcooking, which will lead to mealy, dry meat.

Physically breaking up the muscle fibers in meat is the most direct way to tenderize it. Pounding meat with a mallet, tenderizer, or rolling pin does the trick. Tenderizing in this way is ideal for treating carefully controlled portions. It also spreads the surface area of the meat, making a small portion look bigger. And a thin piece of meat can be cooked quickly, which is helpful for a busy cook.

steak roulade

*Spinach, basil, and gorgonzola wrapped
in steak make a delicious dish any night*

Serves: 4

Prep Time: 20 minutes

Chilling Time: 60 minutes

Cooking Time: 12 to 15 minutes

INGREDIENTS

4 sirloin steaks (1 pound total)

1 teaspoon salt

1/2 teaspoon black pepper

1 10-ounce box chopped-spinach, thawed

3 tablespoons fine bread crumbs

3 tablespoons (**2** oz.) crumbled gorgonzola cheese (any blue cheese or feta will work)

1 clove garlic, minced

2 tablespoons dried basil or **1/8** cup fresh basil, finely chopped

Cooking spray

1. **PREHEAT** oven to 475°F.

2. Lay each steak flat. Cover with a piece of plastic wrap and pound the steak with a meat tenderizer, mallet, or rolling pin to 1/4-inch thickness. **SEASON** each side with the salt and pepper.

3. Squeeze all the extra liquid out of the thawed spinach (you should end up with about a cup of spinach). **COMBINE** the spinach, bread crumbs, gorgonzola cheese, garlic, and basil in a bowl.

4. **SPREAD** a heaping spoonful of the spinach-and-herb mixture over each of the four steaks. Carefully **LIFT** the long side of the steak and **ROLL** it toward the other side, just like a jelly roll. Secure the steak roll with toothpicks or lengths of string. Wrap the steak rolls in plastic wrap and refrigerate 1 hour.

5. Lightly coat the rolled steaks with cooking spray. Place in a roasting pan. **ROAST** 12 to 15 minutes, carefully turning the steak rolls halfway through the cooking process. Let rest 8 minutes and remove strings or toothpicks before slicing and serving.

NUTRITIONAL VALUE PER SERVING			
Calories	270	Total Fat	15g
Carbohydrates	6g	Saturated Fat	7g
Protein	29g	Cholesterol	75mg
Fiber	3g	Sodium	900mg

Exchanges: 1 vegetable, 3 lean meats, 1/2 high-fat meat
Carb Choices: 1/2

While protein is good for you, too much can add excessive saturated fat to your diet.
Here is an elegant, delicious way to make a small portion of steak go a long way:
Enhance it with a flavorful spinach and cheese filling.

country-style steak with onion cream gravy

Savory gravy and tender steak contribute to the charm of this down-home classic

Serves: 4

Prep Time: 10 minutes

Cooking Time: 25 minutes

INGREDIENTS

12 ounces eye round roast

1- 1½ teaspoons black pepper

1 teaspoon salt

3 tablespoons flour

Cooking spray

1½ cups low-fat milk

2 medium onions, peeled

½ cup water

1. TRIM extra fat from the beef. CUT the beef into 8 equal slices. Lay a piece of plastic wrap over each piece and flatten with a mallet or the flat side of a meat tenderizer to ¼-inch thickness. Use the spiked side of the tenderizer to pound each of the flattened pieces. Do not rip the meat. (Flattening and tenderizing the meat allows it to cook quickly with very little oil.) SEASON with ½ teaspoon of pepper and ³⁄4 teaspoon salt.

2. Place the meat and 2 tablespoon of flour in a sealable plastic bag. SHAKE the bag vigorously to coat the meat. WHISK the remaining flour with the milk in a small bowl and set aside.

3. Generously COAT a skillet with cooking spray and HEAT over medium-high heat until very hot. Add the seasoned steaks and brown undisturbed for 45 seconds to 1 minute on each side. Remove from the skillet immediately and set aside.

4. CUT onions lengthwise and then slice into thin strips. Add the onions to the skillet. Reduce the heat to medium and COOK until they are wilted and quite brown, about 15 minutes. ADD the flour-and-milk mixture and stir well. Add the remaining pepper, ¼ teaspoon of salt and ½ cup of water. Cook until the sauce is thickened, about 10 minutes. ADD more water as needed if the sauce becomes too thick. Taste and adjust the salt if needed. Return the steaks to the gravy to heat through. Serve immediately.

Country style steak NUTRITIONAL VALUE PER SERVING			
Calories	190	Total Fat	4g
Carbohydrates	14g	Saturated Fat	1.5g
Protein	23g	Cholesterol	50mg
Fiber	1g	Sodium	670mg

Exchanges: 1 vegetable, ½ milk, 2 lean meats
Carb Choices: 1

what do I do now?

I want to serve my meat piping hot but I'm told I shouldn't slice it right away. What should I do?

When meat is cooked, water in its cells heats and expands and the cells themselves contract. Pressure builds in each cell and some moisture is pushed out of the cells, which is why juice appears in the pan when you cook meat. If you cut a steak or roast straight from the oven, that great juice will run all over the plate and you'll have a dry piece of meat. Instead, let it rest undisturbed with a sheet of foil loosely tenting it. When you do cut the meat, the cells will be relaxed and less moisture will be pushed out. Remember that meat will hold heat and the center will continue to "carryover" cook for a few minutes after it leaves the heat. Let steaks and smaller cuts rest for about half the time they cooked. Large roasts can rest 30 minutes without getting cold.

First Person Disaster: *Cooking for Two*

When my youngest went off to college last year, my husband and I, both Type 2 diabetics, started putting on a few extra pounds. It wasn't until my son asked how I liked cooking for two that I realized I was cooking exactly the same amount! I went to our diabetes educator for help and learned that what I considered a normal portion size was about twice what is considered healthy. With her new portion guidelines in mind, I began to change how I portioned out roasts and steaks. I cut roasts into half-pound chunks, or sliced them into steaks—sometimes pounding them very thin. Then, I individually wrapped them in wax paper and froze stacks of them in sealable plastic bags. I was pleased at how much quicker it was to defrost a half pound roast or $1/4$ inch pork chops than a big piece of meat. Cooking time dropped dramatically too, and I can make dinner in half the time it used to take. The best part is that with portions already measured out, over-eating is no longer an option. The weight is slowly but surely coming off.

–Alysia B., Eufaula, AL

phyllo beef Wellingtons

This dinner party favorite uses light,
flaky phyllo dough instead of puff pastry

Serves: 4

Prep Time: 20 minutes

Cooking Time: 15 minutes

INGREDIENTS

1 pound beef tenderloin

1 teaspoon salt

1/4 teaspoon black pepper

2 teaspoons olive oil

1/2 pound mushrooms, thinly sliced

2 shallots, chopped

1 teaspoon thyme

1 tablespoon Worcestershire sauce

2 tablespoons Parmesan cheese, shredded

8 sheets phyllo dough

Cooking spray

1. **PREHEAT** the oven to 350°F. Slice the tenderloin into 4 equal pieces. **SEASON** with salt and pepper. **HEAT** a heavy skillet over medium-high heat until very hot. Add 1 teaspoon of olive oil and **SEAR** the steaks 45 seconds on each side. Remove from the pan and set aside.

2. **ADD** the remaining olive oil and the mushrooms, shallots, and thyme to the skillet. Reduce heat to medium and **COOK** until all the liquid has evaporated. Add the Worcestershire sauce. Remove from heat and cool slightly before adding the Parmesan cheese. **MIX** well.

3. Lay one sheet of phyllo dough on a flat surface. Coat with cooking spray. Lay another sheet over the top. Coat with cooking spray. Place one seared steak in the center of the sheets. **TOP** with 1/4 of the mushroom mixture. **FOLD** the phyllo over the steak and tuck the edges underneath. You want a smooth phyllo surface. Repeat with the remaining steaks.

4. Arrange the phyllo-wrapped steaks, mushroom side up, on a baking sheet coated with cooking spray. Spray them with cooking spray. **BAKE** 8 to 10 minutes until the phyllo is golden brown.

NUTRITIONAL VALUE PER SERVING

Calories	340	Total Fat	14g
Carbohydrates	24g	Saturated Fat	4.5g
Protein	29g	Cholesterol	75mg
Fiber	2g	Sodium	730mg

Exchanges: 1 1/2 carbohydrates, 1 vegetable, 3 lean meats, 1/2 fat
Carb Choices: 1 1/2

Phyllo is a Greek pastry used in baklava and spanakopita. It is the thin and flaky sheets of dough that can be found in freezer sections of most grocery stores, near the frozen pie dough and puff pastry. Phyllo is low-fat, but a bit tricky to work with. You must work quickly because it is very thin and dries out fast. Keep a damp paper towel over the sheets you're not working with to prevent them from becoming brittle. Here phyllo is used to create a healthful version of the classic beef Wellington.

stir-baked beef and green beans

This fast and flavorful dish is sure to please

Serves: 4

Prep Time: 20 minutes

Cooking Time: 12 minutes

INGREDIENTS

12 ounces skirt steak or very lean sirloin steak

2 teaspoons low-sodium soy sauce

1 teaspoon white wine or rice wine vinegar

1 pound fresh green beans, ends trimmed

2 teaspoons canola oil

Cooking spray

1 tablespoon garlic, finely chopped

1 teaspoon ground ginger or **1** tablespoon fresh ginger, finely chopped

2 stalks green onions, cut into 1-inch lengths

1/2 cup water

1 teaspoon Splenda

1 teaspoon cornstarch

1. With a very sharp knife, cut the beef as thinly as possible across the grain into 2-inch-long strips. In a bowl, COMBINE the meat, 1 teaspoon of the soy sauce, and wine or vinegar. Set aside.

2. TOSS the green beans with 1 teaspoon of canola oil to coat. HEAT a skillet on high. When the skillet is very hot, coat the bottom with cooking spray. Quickly add the beans to the pan and COOK until the beans are wrinkled but still quite crisp, about 6 to 7 minutes. Carefully remove the skillet and spoon out the beans to a large serving platter. Cover the beans to keep them warm.

3. Quickly ADD the remaining teaspoon of oil to the hot skillet. Add the garlic, ginger, and meat. Stir quickly and COOK 2 minutes. Remove the skillet from the heat. The meat should be sizzling and nearly cooked. Add the green onions and stir quickly. Return the skillet to the stove and COOK 2 more minutes, until the meat is completely cooked.

4. Carefully PLACE the meat and onions on top of the cooked green beans and set aside. Place the skillet on the stovetop over medium-high heat. COMBINE the remaining soy sauce with the water, Splenda, and cornstarch in a small bowl. Pour mixture into the skillet and scrape the browned bits of meat, garlic, and ginger off the bottom. Bring to a boil and stir until slightly thickened. Taste the sauce and adjust saltiness, adding a bit of water or more soy sauce as needed. POUR the sauce over the beef and beans. Sprinkle with a few drops of sesame oil if desired. Serve immediately with rice.

Stir-baked beef and green beans
NUTRITIONAL VALUE PER SERVING

Calories	200	Total Fat	9g
Carbohydrates	10g	Saturated Fat	3g
Protein	20g	Cholesterol	50mg
Fiber	3g	Sodium	200mg

Exchanges: 1 vegetable, 2 1/2 lean meats, 1/2 fat
Carb Choices: 1/2

*Chinese takeout can be the downfall of many a conscientious eater because it is
so hard to control your portions. In this dish, just the right amounts of beef and greens
are combined to make a wonderful Asian meal.*

Chapter 7

Poultry

Chicken and turkey are dinnertime favorites. Try these delicious, healthful classics: Chicken and Dumplings (top) and Chicken Cordon Bleu (right).

Italian turkey meatballs

These moist meatballs are great on sand-wiches or with marinara sauce and pasta

Serves: 4

Prep Time: 10 minutes

Cooking Time: 15 minutes

INGREDIENTS

½ cup oats, pulsed in the blender

¼ cup milk

1 pound ground turkey breast

½ cup celery, diced (about half a stalk)

½ cup onion, diced

2 tablespoons fresh parsley, chopped (or 1 tablespoon parsley flakes)

1 teaspoon dried oregano

½ teaspoon dried marjoram

½ teaspoon salt

¼ teaspoon black pepper

Cooking spray

1. PREHEAT the oven to 400° F. COMBINE the pulsed oats and milk in a small bowl and let sit until the milk is absorbed. Combine the turkey and the oat mixture with the remaining ingredients. MIX well. Test the seasoning by cooking a small patty in a pan and adjust the seasoning if needed.

2. Spray baking sheet with cooking spray. With very clean hands, FORM 12 medium or 16 small (walnut-sized) meatballs. Arrange the meatballs on a baking sheet an inch apart and spray with cooking spray. (This will ensure that the meatballs will brown nicely.) COOK 13 to 15 minutes, until the meatballs are browned and cooked through. Serve immediately or cool and store in the refrigerator to use for quick meals during the week.

NUTRITIONAL VALUE PER SERVING			
Calories	210	Total Fat	2.5g
Carbohydrates	16g	Saturated Fat	1g
Protein	30g	Cholesterol	75mg
Fiber	3g	Sodium	360mg

Exchanges: 1 carbohydrate, ½ vegetable, 3 very lean meats
Carb Choices: 1

buffalo chicken nuggets
and light blue-cheese dressing

*These spicy white meat nuggets elevate
a party-time favorite to new heights*

Serves: 4

Prep Time: 7 minutes

Cooking Time: 7 minutes

Marinating time: 60 minutes

INGREDIENTS

1 pound skinless chicken breast

4 tablespoons hot sauce, such as Tabasco, Crystal, or Texas Pete

1/2 cup flour

1/2 teaspoon salt

1/2 teaspoon black pepper

Cooking spray

1 tablespoon margarine

1 teaspoon garlic powder

FOR THE DRESSING

1 cup healthy ranch vinaigrette (see page 72)

2 tablespoons blue cheese, crumbled

1. **CUT** chicken into 1-inch nuggets or 1½-inch strips. In a bowl toss the chicken with 1 tablespoon of the hot sauce and refrigerate at least 1 hour.

2. **PREHEAT** the oven to 450°F. **COMBINE** flour, salt, and pepper in a quart-size self-sealing plastic bag or a lidded plastic container. Add the chicken nuggets, a few at a time, and shake to coat. Arrange chicken nuggets on a baking sheet coated with cooking spray. **COAT** chicken with cooking spray.

3. **BAKE** 3 minutes, then carefully flip the nuggets. Bake another 3 minutes or until the chicken is firm to the touch and slightly browned. **CUT** open a piece to check for doneness if you are uncertain.

4. **ADD** the blue cheese to the healthy ranch dressing in a small bowl, and set aside.

5. In a microwave-safe bowl, **COMBINE** the margarine, garlic powder, and remaining hot sauce. Microwave 30 seconds or until the margarine is melted and the sauce is heated.

6. When the chicken is cooked, immediately transfer it to a large bowl. **ADD** the hot sauce mixture and toss to coat the chicken. Transfer to a platter and serve at once with celery and carrot sticks and blue cheese dressing.

NUTRITIONAL VALUE PER SERVING WITH DRESSING			
Calories	290	Total Fat	9g
Carbohydrates	21g	Saturated Fat	2.5g
Protein	27g	Cholesterol	70mg
Fiber	1g	Sodium	750mg

Exchanges: 1 carbohydrate, 1/2 other carbohydrate, 3 very lean meats, 1 fat
Carb Choices: 1 1/2

oven-fried chicken tenders
and sweet mustard sauce

*These crunchy, juicy strips will be a hit
with children and adults alike*

Serves: 4

Prep Time: 7 minutes

Cooking Time: 8 minutes

INGREDIENTS

2 egg whites

1/4 cup water

1 1/2 cups cornflakes cereal

2 tablespoons flour

1 teaspoon salt

1/2 teaspoon black pepper

1 pound chicken, tenders
or breast, cut in long
strips

Cooking spray

2/3 cup sweet mustard
sauce

SWEET MUSTARD SAUCE

1/4 cup nonfat mayon-
naise

1 1/2 tablespoons Dijon
mustard

1 tablespoon red onion,
finely diced

2 teaspoons red wine
vinegar

2 teaspoons water

1 packet Equal

1/8 teaspoon cayenne
pepper

dash of black pepper

1. PREHEAT oven to 475°F. In a bowl, WHISK together the egg whites and water.

2. Put the cornflakes in a plastic zipper-close bag and crush them finely with a rolling pin. ADD the flour, 1/2 teaspoon salt, and the black pepper to the bag and SHAKE to mix.

3. If you're using tenders, remove the tough white tendon that runs the length of the meat. SEASON the chicken with 1/2 teaspoon of salt. DIP the chicken in the egg wash and shake off any excess.

4. Drop the chicken in the plastic bag with the cornflake mixture and SHAKE to coat completely. Work in batches if necessary.

5. Arrange the breaded tenders on a baking sheet coated with cooking spray. Thoroughly COAT the tenders with cooking spray. BAKE 5 minutes. Turn the tenders and bake another 3 minutes until firm and browned. Serve hot with sweet mustard sauce.

SWEET MUSTARD SAUCE
Serves: 4-6   Prep Time: 6 minutes

1. WHISK all ingredients together in a small bowl.

2. Serve immediately or store in the refrigerator for use any time. For a thinner, more pourable sauce, ADD 2 to 3 tablespoons more water.

Makes 2/3 cup.

Oven-fried chicken tenders with sweet mustard sauce NUTRITIONAL VALUE PER SERVING			
Calories	210	Total Fat	3.5g
Carbohydrates	16g	Saturated Fat	1g
Protein	26g	Cholesterol	65mg
Fiber	0g	Sodium	1040mg

Exchanges: 1 carbohydrate, 3 very lean meats
Carb Choices: 1

This crunchy chicken is oven-fried. When served with this sweet and savory dipping sauce, it is a meal fit for the finickiest of little eaters.

Sweet Mustard Sauce by itself **NUTRITIONAL VALUE PER TABLESPOON**			
Calories	10	Total Fat	0g
Carbohydrates	1g	Saturated Fat	0g
Protein	0g	Cholesterol	0mg
Fiber	0g	Sodium	100mg
Exchanges: 0 Carb Choices: 0			

turkey shepherd's pie

Mashed potatoes complement lean turkey breast in a comforting meal for a cold day

Serves: 6

Prep Time: 20 minutes

Cooking Time: 60 minutes

INGREDIENTS

2 large potatoes, peeled and diced

Cooking spray

1.5 pounds ground turkey breast

1 cup onion, diced

1 cup celery, diced

1 cup carrots, diced

2 cups mushrooms, cleaned, stems removed, and chopped

2 tablespoons flour

1½ teaspoon ground sage

½ teaspoon dried thyme

3 cups low-sodium chicken broth

1½ cups peas (fresh or frozen)

½ teaspoon black pepper

½ cup low-fat milk

2 tablespoons light margarine

½ teaspoon salt

1. **PREHEAT** oven to 350° F. Put the potatoes in a large pot. **COVER** them with cold water and set on a burner to boil.

2. Coat the bottom of a large skillet with cooking spray. Place over medium-high heat and add the turkey. **COOK**, stirring often and breaking the meat into small pieces. Remove the cooked turkey from the skillet and set aside.

3. **ADD** a little more cooking spray to the skillet. Add the onion, celery and carrots. **COOK**, stirring often, until the vegetables have softened and begun to brown on the edges, about 7 minutes. Add the mushrooms and cook 5 minutes longer. Add the flour and mix well to coat the vegetables. Add the sage, thyme, and chicken broth. **STIR** well and bring to a boil. Reduce heat and **SIMMER** 5 minutes, until the sauce has slightly reduced and thickened. Add the peas and the cooked turkey meat. Add the black pepper. Taste and adjust the seasoning as needed. **POUR** the turkey mixture into a casserole dish or an 8 by 8 glass baking dish.

4. The potatoes should be very tender by now. Drain, reserving about ¼ cup of the boiling water. Add the milk, margarine, and salt to the potatoes. **MASH** with a whisk or potato masher until almost smooth. Add a little of the reserved potato water if they seem too stiff. **WHIP** with an electric mixer on low. Taste and adjust the seasoning as needed. Spoon the mashed potatoes over the turkey mixture, and **SPREAD** with a rubber spatula, completely covering the turkey. With the back of a fork, make a crosshatch or herringbone pattern in the potatoes. **BAKE** 25 to 30 minutes, until the mashed potatoes have browned. Serve warm with a fresh salad.

Turkey shepherd's pie **NUTRITIONAL VALUE PER SERVING**			
Calories	340	Total Fat	4g
Carbohydrates	38g	Saturated Fat	1g
Protein	38g	Cholesterol	85mg
Fiber	7g	Sodium	390mg

Exchanges: 2 carbohydrates, 1½ vegetables, 3 very lean meats, 1 fat
Carb Choices: 2½

This shepherd's pie packs vegetables and low-fat ground turkey into a healthful one-dish meal. If you are short on time, use frozen or instant mashed potatoes.

Thai turkey curry

Coconut milk, basil, and a little spice combine in this unique Asian dish

Serves: 4

Prep Time: 5 minutes

Cooking Time: 30 minutes

INGREDIENTS

1 pound ground turkey breast

2 tablespoons Splenda

2 tablespoons low-sodium soy sauce

1 tablespoon canola oil

4 cloves garlic, minced

2 shallots, minced (or **1** medium yellow onion)

1 tablespoon fresh ginger, grated

1/4 cup sweet red pepper, diced

1/4 teaspoon dried red pepper flakes

2 tablespoons dried basil

1 cup low-sodium chicken broth

1/2 tablespoon cornstarch

1/2 cup low-fat, non-sweetened coconut milk (shake the can before opening)

1. **COMBINE** the turkey, Splenda, and 1 tablespoon of soy sauce. Mix well and set aside. Heat a nonstick skillet over medium-high heat. Add the canola oil. Add the garlic, shallots, and ginger. **COOK** until translucent and fragrant, about 2 minutes. Add the red pepper and dried pepper flakes and basil and **COOK** 1 minute more.

2. **ADD** the turkey mixture and brown, breaking up the meat into very small pieces, about 5 minutes.

3. **MIX** the broth and cornstarch. Add the broth mixture to the turkey. Add 1 tablespoon more soy sauce. **COOK** until the sauce begins to thicken and the flavors come together.

4. Add the coconut milk. **HEAT** through. Taste and season with salt as needed. Serve with brown rice.

NUTRITIONAL VALUE PER SERVING			
Calories	220	Total Fat	7g
Carbohydrates	7g	Saturated Fat	2.5g
Protein	31g	Cholesterol	85mg
Fiber	1g	Sodium	530mg

Exchanges: 1/2 vegetable, 3 very lean meats, 1 fat
Carb Choices: 1/2

what is it  and where do I get it?

How do I know what herbs and spices to use in my cooking?

When you're experimenting with recipes, there really are no wrong answers. However, some flavors are more commonly associated with certain cuisines. This chart might help you with the basics.

CAJUN: cayenne pepper, black pepper, celery, green pepper, onion, bay leaves, hot sauces

CARIBBEAN: allspice, thyme, hot peppers, lime, cumin

CHINESE: garlic, ginger, scallion, five-spice powder, sesame oils, soy sauces

GREEK: oregano, cumin, rosemary, marjoram, honey, olives

FRENCH: sage, thyme, rosemary, tarragon, dill, parsley, basil, oregano

INDIAN: coriander, curry powder, cumin, turmeric, gingerroot, ground ginger, garlic, mustard seed

ITALIAN: oregano, basil, thyme, garlic, flat leaf-parsley

JAPANESE: soy sauce, sake, mirin, miso, gingerroot, sesame seeds

MEXICAN: cumin, oregano, basil, cilantro, lime, fresh and dried peppers

MIDDLE EASTERN: cumin, sesame paste (tahini), cinnamon, cardamom, cloves, mint, lemon, thyme

SOUTHEAST ASIAN: ginger, lemon grass, fresh basil, garlic, coconut milk, mint, cilantro, fish sauce

chicken cordon bleu

The combination of chicken, cheese, and ham makes an elegant dish for any occasion

Serves: 4

Prep Time: 15 minutes

Cooking Time: 20 minutes

INGREDIENTS

4 thin chicken cutlets (**1** pound) or **2** large boneless skinless chicken breasts, halved and pounded 1/4 inch thick

4 large, thin slices deli ham

4 thin slices Swiss cheese or 1/2 cup low-fat Swiss cheese, grated

2 egg whites, beaten

1/4 cup water

1/2 teaspoon salt

1/2 cup fine bread crumbs

1/2 teaspoon dried thyme

Cooking spray

1. **PREHEAT** oven to 400°F.

2. **Lay** each chicken breast on a cutting board. Lay a slice of deli ham on each chicken cutlet. Place a slice of cheese on top of the ham slice. **ROLL** the chicken breast up like a jelly roll and **SECURE** the seam with a toothpick.

3. In a small bowl, **WHISK** together the egg whites, water, and a dash of salt. In a separate bowl, **COMBINE** the bread crumbs, remaining salt, and thyme.

4. Arrange the chicken rolls, egg wash, and bread crumbs in a row in front of you. Working as neatly as possible, **DIP** the chicken rolls in the egg wash. Shake off the excess and **COAT** in the bread crumbs. Lay the breaded chicken roll on a baking sheet lightly coated with cooking spray. Continue coating the rest of the chicken.

5. Lightly **COAT** the breaded chicken with cooking spray. **BAKE** for 10 minutes. Carefully flip the chicken rolls and bake another 8 to 10 minutes, until the meat is firm to the touch and the breading has browned. Serve with springy succotash (see page 169).

NUTRITIONAL VALUE PER SERVING			
Calories	260	Total Fat	8g
Carbohydrates	11g	Saturated Fat	3.5g
Protein	35g	Cholesterol	90mg
Fiber	0g	Sodium	900mg

Exchanges: 1 carbohydrate, 3 very lean meats, 1 lean meat, 1/2 high-fat meat
Carb Choices: 1

So elegant yet so simple to make, this Chicken Cordon Bleu makes an ideal dinner-party entree.

chicken and mushroom cream sauce over fettuccini

Your guests will never know this fragrant and creamy dish is healthy

Serves: 4

Prep Time: 5 minutes

Cooking Time: 25 minutes

INGREDIENTS

1 pound boneless, skinless chicken breasts, cut into bite-size pieces

1/2 teaspoon salt

1/4 teaspoon black pepper

2 teaspoons dried rosemary

Cooking spray

2 large shallots, chopped fine (or **1/2 cup** yellow onion, chopped)

1 teaspoon light margarine

1 pound white mushrooms, stems removed, cut into bite-size pieces

1/4 cup dry white wine

1 cup low-sodium chicken broth

1 tablespoon cornstarch

1 cup low-fat milk

1/2 pound fettuccini, cooked

1. **SEASON** the chicken pieces with the salt and black pepper and half the rosemary. (To better release its flavor, crush the rosemary in your palm before adding it to the chicken.) **HEAT** a deep skillet over medium-high heat and generously coat it with cooking spray. Add the chicken to the hot skillet and **BROWN** it quickly, stirring every 10 seconds or so. As soon as the chicken has browned on all sides, remove it from the pan and set aside. The chicken should not be cooked through.

2. Add the shallots and margarine to the skillet. **COOK** until softened, about 3 minutes. Add the mushrooms and **COOK** until they start to give off their liquid and begin to brown, about 6 minutes. Add the remaining rosemary and the wine and **SCRAPE** the browned bits off the bottom of the pan. Cook until the wine has reduced and the pan is almost dry.

3. **MIX** the broth and cornstarch and add to the pan. **COOK** until the liquid has thickened, about 2 minutes. Add the milk and stir. **SIMMER** until the sauce looks smooth and slightly thickened.

4. Return the browned chicken to the mushroom sauce. **SIMMER** until the chicken is cooked through, about 5 minutes. Serve sauce ladled over fettuccini.

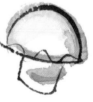

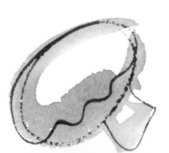

what do I do now?

Why is skinless poultry better for you than poultry with skin?

Two reasons: calories and saturated fat. Here's a comparison of the calories, fat, cholesterol, and protein contained in a 3.5-ounce serving of chicken breast roasted with and without the skin.

	Breast with Skins	**Breast without Skins**
Calories:	197	165
Fat:	7.8 g	3.6 g
Protein:	30 g	27 g
Cholesterol:	85 mg	85 mg

Figures come from the USDA's National Nutrient Database for Standard Reference

How does cornstarch work in a recipe?

You can use cornstarch to thicken a sauce, instead of using cheese, cream, or butter. A sauce thickened with cornstarch will have a nice smooth, creamy texture without the added fat. Cornstarch contains 7 grams of carbohydrate per tablespoon, slightly higher than flour, which is also a thickener. But the thickening power of cornstarch is amazing, and you'll need only half as much cornstarch as flour to thicken the same amount of liquid.

Chicken and mushroom cream sauce over fettuccini NUTRITIONAL VALUE PER SERVING			
Calories	410	Total Fat	5g
Carbohydrates	54g	Saturated Fat	1.5g
Protein	38g	Cholesterol	65mg
Fiber	9g	Sodium	420mg

Exchanges: 3 carbohydrates, 1 vegetable, 3 very lean meats
Carb Choices: 3 1/2

turkey scallopini

Lean turkey cooked on high heat makes
tender cutlets for pasta dishes or sandwiches

Serves: 4-6

Prep Time: 15 minutes

Cooking Time: 6 minutes

INGREDIENTS

1½ pounds boneless turkey breast (or chicken breast)

1 teaspoon salt

2 egg whites, beaten

¼ cup water

1 cup fine bread crumbs

1 tablespoon Parmesan or Romano cheese, grated

2 teaspoons dried basil

½ teaspoon garlic powder

Cooking spray

1. PREHEAT oven to 450°F. Slice the turkey breast into ½-inch slices. Gently but firmly pound the turkey between sheets of plastic wrap with a flat mallet or rolling pin. Pound the turkey to a ¼-inch thickness. If you're using chicken, lay each chicken breast on the cutting board and SLICE in half, holding the knife parallel to the cutting board. Pound the breasts to ¼-inch thickness. SEASON the turkey or chicken lightly with ½ teaspoon salt.

2. WHISK the egg whites and water until smooth. Add a dash of salt. In a separate bowl, COMBINE the bread crumbs, grated cheese, basil, garlic powder, and the remaining salt.

3. ARRANGE the pounded turkey, egg wash, and bread crumb mixture in a row in front of you. Working as neatly as possible, dip the chicken in the egg wash. SHAKE off the excess and COAT in the bread crumbs. Lay the breaded breast on a baking sheet lightly coated with cooking spray. Continue coating the rest of the turkey

4. COAT the turkey lightly with cooking spray. BAKE for 4 minutes. Carefully flip the breasts and bake another 2 minutes, until the meat is firm to the touch and the breading has browned. Serve with spaghetti and marinara sauce, on a submarine sandwich or on its own with a squeeze of fresh lemon juice, roasted potatoes, and steamed vegetables.

NUTRITIONAL VALUE PER SERVING			
Calories	220	Total Fat	2g
Carbohydrates	14g	Saturated Fat	0.5g
Protein	34g	Cholesterol	85mg
Fiber	0g	Sodium	630mg

Exchanges: 1 carbohydrate, 3 very lean meats
Carb Choices: 1

what is it  and where do I get it?

WHITE OR DARK MEAT

Most people know whether they prefer white or dark meat on a Thanksgiving turkey, but not everyone knows what exactly makes white or dark meat different. In chickens and turkeys, "white" meat comes mainly from the little-used breast muscles of these flightless birds. Dark meat comes from leg and thigh muscles. These muscles on the bird get used more often and are aided by extra oxygen stored in their cells. This extra oxygen makes the meat dark red, hence "dark" meat. Nutritionally, the extra fat fueling these muscles makes dark meat higher in calories.

Here's how the fat, calories, and protein in a 3.5-ounce serving of roasted "white" meat stacks up to the same amount of roasted "dark" meat:

	White Meat	Dark Meat
Protein:	31 g	27 g
Calories:	165	205
Fat:	3.6 g	9.7 g
Cholesterol:	85 mg	93 mg

Figures come from the USDA's National Nutrient Database for Standard Reference

chicken and dumplings

*Baked to perfection, dumplings provide a
little crunch to this down-home favorite*

Serves: 6

Prep Time: 15 minutes

Cooking Time: 50 minutes

INGREDIENTS

1 cup onion, diced small

½ cup carrot, sliced thin
(about 1 carrot)

½ cup celery, diced small
(about 1 stalk)

1 cup flour, plus **2**
tablespoons

2 teaspoons dried thyme

2 teaspoons dried sage

2 cups low-sodium
chicken broth

1 bay leaf

1¼ teaspoons baking
powder

1½ teaspoons salt

3 tablespoons butter or
margarine, diced and well
chilled

½–¾ cup low-fat milk

1½ pound chicken breast
or breast tenders, cubed

1 cup frozen corn, thawed

1 cup frozen peas, thawed

Cooking spray

1. PREHEAT oven to 425°F. Have a baking dish or casserole dish
ready for later. Coat a large skillet with cooking spray and **HEAT** over
medium-high heat. Add the onion, carrot, and celery and **COOK** until
the vegetables are softened and browned on the edges, about 6 minutes. Add 2 tablespoons of flour, thyme, and sage. Mix to coat the
vegetables. **COOK** another 3 to 4 minutes, stirring often. Add the
chicken broth and the bay leaf and stir well. **SIMMER** 10 minutes.

2. While the broth simmers, **WHISK** together 1 cup of flour, the baking
powder, and ½ teaspoon of salt. Working quickly, add the butter to
the flour mixture and crumble it into the flour. **WORK** the butter and
flour between your fingers until it is the texture of bread crumbs. You
don't want the butter to melt, so **PLACE** the whole bowl in the freezer
for 5 minutes if you think it's getting too warm. Make a well in the
middle of the flour mixture and add the milk slowly, mixing in the
flour as you go. The dough should be very soft and sticky. Let it sit in
the refrigerator until you're ready to use it.

3. ADD the raw cubed chicken to the skillet and the remaining 1 teaspoon of salt. Taste and adjust the salt as needed. **COOK** about 3 minutes, until the chicken is just barely cooked. (You'll bake the chicken
later so it's better for it to be undercooked at this stage.) Mix in the
corn and peas.

4. Transfer the chicken and vegetable mixture to a baking dish. **SCOOP**
a heaping tablespoon of the chilled dumpling batter onto the top of
the stew. Repeat with the rest of the dough. You should have enough
dough to make 8 to 12 dumplings. Spray the top of the dumplings
lightly with cooking spray. **BAKE** the chicken and dumplings 20 minutes, until the dumplings are puffy and browned on top and the stew
is bubbling. Serve right from the oven.

Nothing says home like a meal of Chicken and Dumplings. If you are pressed for time, use refrigerator biscuits for the topping.

Chicken and dumplings
NUTRITIONAL VALUE PER SERVING

Calories	300	Total Fat	9g
Carbohydrates	32g	Saturated Fat	4.5g
Protein	24g	Cholesterol	65mg
Fiber	3g	Sodium	790mg

Exchanges: 2 carbohydrates, 1 vegetable, 3 very lean meats, 2 fats
Carb Choices: 2

kung pao chicken

The crunch of peanuts and water chestnuts make this takeout favorite an at-home winner

Serves: 4

Prep Time: 10 minutes

Cooking Time: 15 minutes

Marinating Time: 30 minutes

INGREDIENTS

1 pound boneless, skinless, chicken breast, cubed

1 egg white, lightly beaten

2 teaspoons cornstarch

3 teaspoons sherry or dry white wine

1 teaspoon Splenda

1 tablespoon black bean sauce (see next page)

1/4 cup low-sodium chicken broth

1 teaspoon rice vinegar

Cooking spray

1/2 medium onion, chopped

2 cloves garlic, minced

1 teaspoon ground ginger

1/2 cup dry roasted peanuts

1 8-ounce can water chestnuts, drained and quartered

Red pepper flakes

1. **COMBINE** the chicken, egg white, cornstarch, sherry or white wine, and Splenda in bowl and **MARINATE** for 30 minutes at room temperature. In a separate bowl, prepare the sauce by mixing the black bean sauce, chicken broth, and rice vinegar.

2. **HEAT** a wok or large nonstick skillet over high heat. **COAT** generously with cooking spray and add the chicken. **BROWN** the chicken, turning every 10 seconds until all sides are browned but the chicken is not cooked through. Remove from the pan and set aside.

3. Add the onions and **COOK**, stirring often, until they begin to brown on the edges. Add the garlic and ginger and **STIR** quickly, being careful not to burn the garlic. Add the peanuts and water chestnuts. Stir vigorously until the peanuts and water chestnuts are slightly browned. Return the chicken to the pan. Add the sauce and stir well. Add red pepper flakes for spiciness and **COOK** until the chicken is completely done and the sauce has thickened. If the sauce looks too thick, **ADD** a little more broth and stir well. Serve immediately over steamed rice.

NUTRITIONAL VALUE PER SERVING			
Calories	290	Total Fat	12g
Carbohydrates	13g	Saturated Fat	2g
Protein	32g	Cholesterol	70mg
Fiber	4g	Sodium	115mg

Exchanges: 1 other carbohydrate, 3 very lean meats, 1/2 fat
Carb Choices: 1

what is it and where do I get it?

BLACK BEAN SAUCE

Black bean sauce or paste is made from salt-preserved black soybeans. The pungent, salty paste is used in many Chinese dishes. It can be found in the Asian section of many large grocery stores or in Asian markets. As the sodium content is quite high and the flavor very strong, a little goes a long way. If you don't have the black bean sauce needed to make kung pao chicken, just add an extra $1/2$ tablespoon dark soy sauce and $1/2$ teaspoon cornstarch to the sauce.

First Person Disaster: *Cook Once, Eat Twice*

When I went back to work after my children reached school age, I began cooking large meals to ensure leftovers for dinners later in the week. The problem was that on "leftover night" my family complained about a "warmed over" flavor, especially with chicken dishes. I started doing some research and found that there are some ways to cook chicken so the leftovers taste better. First, I try to avoid using iron or aluminum pots when cooking because these metals can react with natural fats in the meat and produce an "off" flavor when they sit in the refrigerator. Salt can do the same thing, so I try to avoid salting the portion I'll be saving. Recipes using onions and peppers make good leftovers since these vegetables prevent fats from breaking down. And of course storing leftovers in airtight containers helps too. Now my family happily gobbles up chicken leftovers.

—Lisa H., Manassas, VA

golden tomato Swiss chicken

Swiss cheese and balsamic vinegar form a delicious crust on this chicken dish

Serves: 4

Prep Time: 5 minutes

Cooking Time: 8-10 minutes

INGREDIENTS

Cooking spray

4 boneless, skinless chicken cutlets (1 pound)

1/2 teaspoon salt

1/4 teaspoon black pepper

1 small onion, sliced in rings

2 teaspoons balsamic vinegar

12 fresh basil leaves

5 very thin deli slices of Swiss cheese or 5 tablespoons shredded mozzarella

1 medium ripe tomato, sliced thin

1. **PREHEAT** oven to 475°F. Lightly coat a heavy baking sheet with cooking spray.

2. **SEASON** the cutlets with salt and pepper. Arrange the chicken fillets on the baking sheet so they do not touch.

3. Arrange several slices of onion on each chicken breast. Sprinkle 1/2 teaspoon of balsamic vinegar over each breast. Rip 8 of the basil leaves and distribute over the chicken. **LAY** one slice of cheese on top of the chicken. Lay 2 slices of tomato on top of the cheese.

4. **CUT** the last slice of cheese into 4 parts and **TOP** each chicken breast with a bit of cheese and the remaining basil leaves. **BAKE** 8 to 10 minutes, until the chicken is firm and the tomatoes have shriveled a little. Serve hot with salad and bread or pasta.

NUTRITIONAL VALUE PER SERVING			
Calories	190	Total Fat	7g
Carbohydrates	4g	Saturated Fat	3.5g
Protein	27g	Cholesterol	75mg
Fiber	0g	Sodium	390mg

Exchanges: 1/2 vegetable, 3 very lean meats, 1/2 high-fat meat
Carb Choices: 1/2

artichoke chicken breasts

Sautéing the vegetables and then roasting them in a hot oven concentrates their sunny flavors

Serves: 4

Prep Time: 6 minutes

Cooking Time: 15 minutes

INGREDIENTS

4 boneless, skinless chicken cutlets (1 pound)

1/2 teaspoon salt

1/4 teaspoon black pepper

1 15-ounce can artichoke hearts, drained (marinated artichokes can be used; drain and rinse lightly)

Cooking spray

1 medium onion, diced (about 1 cup)

1 large ripe tomato, diced (canned tomatoes, diced and drained, can be substituted)

1 cup mushrooms, sliced

1 clove garlic, thinly sliced

1 teaspoon dried oregano

1/2 teaspoon dried thyme

1. **PREHEAT** oven to 500°F. **SEASON** both sides of the chicken cutlets with salt and pepper and set aside.

2. Coarsely **CHOP** the artichoke hearts

3. **HEAT** a large oven-safe skillet over medium-high heat. Coat with cooking spray. Add the onion pieces and **COOK** until they begin to brown at the edges. **ADD** the tomato, artichokes, mushrooms, garlic, oregano, and thyme. Sauté until all the vegetables soften and the mushrooms brown slightly at the edges (about 6 to 8 minutes total). The tomatoes and mushrooms should give off some liquid. Let the liquid thicken slightly.

4. Nestle the chicken breasts in the skillet with the artichoke mixture distributed around the chicken. **PLACE** in the oven for 6 to 8 minutes, until the chicken is firm to the touch.

5. To serve, turn each chicken breast over on a plate to present the prettier, browned side. **SCOOP** some of the vegetable mixture around and over each piece of chicken. Garnish with fresh herbs or a slice of lemon. Serve with a green salad and a slice of crunchy French bread.

NUTRITIONAL VALUE PER SERVING

Calories	200	Total Fat	3g
Carbohydrates	15g	Saturated Fat	1g
Protein	30g	Cholesterol	65mg
Fiber	5g	Sodium	870mg

Exchanges: 3 vegetables, 3 very lean meats
Carb Choices: 1

Chapter 8

Seafood

Seafood is so fast and easy to prepare. Better still, it is a wonderful source of low-fat protein. Try these delicious entrees: Shrimp Louis (top) and Sweet and Savory Roasted Salmon (right).

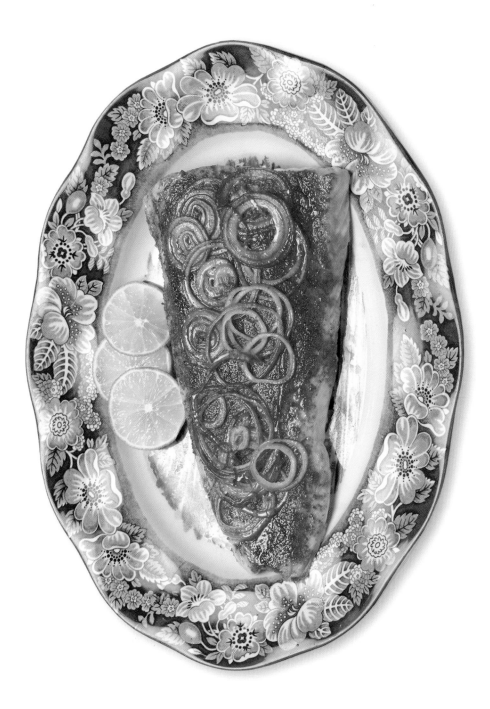

steamed mussels in white-wine tomato broth

Serve with crusty French bread to soak up the delicious broth

Serves: 6 as a starter
3 as a meal

Prep Time: 5 minutes

Cooking Time: 20 minutes

INGREDIENTS

1 tablespoon olive oil

3 cloves garlic, peeled and sliced

2 ripe Roma tomatoes, diced

1 cup dry white wine (a bottle of good lager or pale ale beer can be substituted)

1 bay leaf

2 pounds mussels, scrubbed and debearded

1 to 2 cups water

1 tablespoon butter

1/4 teaspoon salt

1. In a large lidded pot, **HEAT** the olive oil over medium-high heat. Add the garlic and **COOK** for one minute until the garlic is fragrant and softened but not browned. Add the tomatoes and **COOK**, stirring often, until the tomatoes are slightly softened, about 2 minutes. Add the wine or beer and **SCRAPE** up any tomato bits stuck to the bottom of the pan. Add the bay leaf. Let the wine reduce by about half.

2. **ADD** the mussels and give them a toss to coat. Add just enough water to barely cover the mussels at the bottom of the pot. Depending on the size of your pot, this will probably be about 1 1/2 to 2 cups. **COVER** and turn the heat to high.

3. When the broth is boiling vigorously (there'll be a lot of steam escaping from the lid), **REDUCE** the heat to medium-high and **STEAM** about 8 minutes, carefully shaking the closed pot halfway through to redistribute the mussels.

4. **REMOVE** the lid carefully. The mussels are cooked when their shells have opened. If none of the shells have opened yet, **RETURN** the cover and cook another 2 to 3 minutes.

5. Being careful to avoid scooping up any sand that might have collected in the bottom of the pot, **SCOOP** the mussels from the pot with a skimmer or a large slotted spoon. Put them in a deep serving dish or in individual bowls. Then ladle the broth into another bowl or pot (again avoiding any sand in the bottom of the cooking pot) and **WHISK** in the butter and salt. **LADLE** the broth over the mussels. Serve immediately with hot sourdough bread and salad.

NUTRITIONAL VALUE PER SERVING			
Calories	210	Total Fat	10g
Carbohydrates	6g	Saturated Fat	3.5g
Protein	10g	Cholesterol	30mg
Fiber	0g	Sodium	420mg

Exchanges: 1 vegetable, 2 very lean meats, 2 fats
Carb Choices: 1/2

what do I do now?

How do I debeard a mussel?

Most of the mussels you buy in the grocery store are already cleaned and debearded. (The "beard" is the dark threads that hang from the mussel's shell.) If you should get bearded ones, here's how to ready them for cooking:

1. Soak the mussels in fresh water for 15 minutes to remove excess sand.

2. With needle-nose pliers or your fingers, take hold of the "beard." Yank the threads toward the hinge end of the mussel to remove.

3. Use a brush to clean off any barnacles or dirt from the shells.

4. Rinse under cold water and dry on a paper towel before cooking.

First Person Disaster: *Fresh Idea for a Fresh Catch*

After a successful fishing trip, my husband brought home 30 pounds of sea bass fillets. We rinsed the fish and carefully wrapped it for the freezer. A couple of weeks later we cooked a few pieces and were disappointed in the flavor. I'd thawed the fish in the refrigerator, but the fish tasted and smelled a little stronger than I prefer. It just didn't taste fresh-caught like it did when my husband first brought it home. My sister suggested that the next time I thaw it in milk. I did just that, rinsing it thoroughly before cooking, and the fish tasted wonderful! This is definitely the way to get the most out of frozen fish.

—Jess M., Charlotte, NC

deviled fish cakes

Dress up these lightly breaded patties for an elegant meal or a sandwich with tartar sauce

Serves: 4

Prep Time: 20 minutes

Cooking Time: 20 minutes

Chilling Time: 30 minutes

INGREDIENTS

2 cloves of garlic, minced

$\frac{1}{2}$ red onion, diced small

$\frac{1}{2}$ green bell pepper, diced small

$\frac{1}{2}$ red bell pepper, diced small

1 pound flounder fillets (tilapia or halibut may be substituted)

1 egg white, beaten

$\frac{1}{4}$ cup nonfat mayonnaise

1 tablespoon lemon juice

$\frac{1}{4}$ teaspoon salt

1 cup cornbread crumbs

Cooking spray

1. COAT a nonstick skillet with cooking spray and place over medium heat. ADD the garlic and vegetables and sauté until softened, about 8 minutes. COOL to room temperature.

2. Coarsely CHOP the fish and add to a food processor or blender. ADD the egg white. Pulse several times until the fish is broken up but not pureed. Transfer to a bowl and add the mayonnaise, lemon juice, salt, and cooled vegetables. MIX very well.

3. CHILL the mixture for 30 minutes. With clean hands, FORM mixture into 8 patties. POUR the cornbread crumbs into a shallow dish. Press the patties into the crumbs to coat all sides.

4. PREHEAT oven to 425°F. COAT a foil-lined baking sheet with cooking spray. Arrange the fish cakes on the sheet. COAT the fish cakes with cooking spray. BAKE 15 to 20 minutes, turning halfway through, until golden brown and hot. Serve with tartar sauce and coleslaw.

NUTRITIONAL VALUE PER SERVING			
Calories	210	Total Fat	4.5g
Carbohydrates	20g	Saturated Fat	1g
Protein	22g	Cholesterol	70mg
Fiber	2g	Sodium	590mg

Exchanges: 1 carbohydrate, 1 vegetable, 3 very lean meats
Carb Choices: 1 $\frac{1}{2}$

These fish cakes are a snap to make and fun to eat—a perfect treat
that turns inexpensive fillets of fish into a delectable meal. Serve
them with Light Coleslaw (see page 76).

baby shrimp and snow peas

Sweet shrimp and crispy snow peas are a great combination in this classic stir-fry

Serves: 4

Prep Time: 6 minutes

Cooking Time: 10 minutes

Marinating Time: 15 minutes

INGREDIENTS

1 egg white, beaten

1 tablespoon cornstarch

1 teaspoon rice vinegar or white wine vinegar

1 teaspoon Splenda

2 cloves garlic, chopped

1 teaspoon ground ginger or **2** teaspoons fresh ginger, minced

1 pound small shrimp, thawed and prepeeled

1/2 pound green snow peas

Cooking spray

1 cup low-sodium chicken stock

1/4 teaspoon salt

1/2 teaspoon sesame oil

3 cups long grain rice, steamed

1. In a large bowl, **COMBINE** the egg white, cornstarch, vinegar, Splenda, and half the garlic and half the ginger. Add the shrimp. Mix well and **MARINATE** 15 minutes at room temperature.

2. **RINSE** the snow peas and snap the ends, pulling off the tough fiber that runs along the curve of the pea. Plunge the snow peas in boiling water for 30 seconds or microwave them on high with a tablespoon of water for 1 minute. Immediately **RUN** cold water over the snow peas to stop the cooking so they will keep their bright green color.

3. **HEAT** a wok or large skillet over high heat. **COAT** generously with cooking spray. Add the shrimp and **STIR-FRY** quickly, shaking the pan and tossing the shrimp vigorously, for 1 minute. Add the remaining garlic, ginger, and the partially cooked snow peas. Toss vigorously. Add about a quarter of the chicken stock to produce some steam and loosen any shrimp stuck to the pan. **COOK** about 2 more minutes.

4. **ADD** the rest of the chicken stock, a quarter at a time until there is a nicely thickened sauce coating the shrimp and snow peas. Add the salt. Taste and adjust the salt if necessary. **TRANSFER** to a serving plate and drizzle with sesame oil. Garnish with chopped green onions if dsired. Serve at once over steamed rice.

NUTRITIONAL VALUE PER SERVING			
Calories	330	Total Fat	3.5g
Carbohydrates	41g	Saturated Fat	0.5g
Protein	30g	Cholesterol	170mg
Fiber	2g	Sodium	350mg

Exchanges: 2 1/2 carbohydrates, 1/2 vegetable, 3 very lean meats
Carb Choices: 2 1/2

tilapia tacos

*Use the broiler to create this spicy
Californian favorite*

Serves: 4

Prep Time: 15 minutes

Cooking Time: 7 minutes

Marinating Time: 60 minutes

INGREDIENTS

2 cloves garlic, diced

1 tablespoon chili powder

1 teaspoon cumin

1/2 teaspoon salt

2 limes

1 tablespoon canola oil

1 pound tilapia fillets
(or snapper fillets)

8-12 4-inch corn tortillas

1. **COMBINE** the garlic, chili powder, cumin, salt, and juice of 2 limes. Coat the fish with this spicy lime mixture. **MARINATE**, covered, in the refrigerator 1 hour.

2. You can grill this fish or broil it in the oven. If grilling, rub the grill with oil when the coals are ready. Rub 1 tablespoon of canola oil over the fish before grilling. **GRILL** 2 minutes per side for thin fillets, 3 minutes for thicker ones. To broil, **PREHEAT** the broiler and move the broiler rack as close to the heat source as possible. Rub the fish with canola oil before broiling. **COOK** on an oiled broiler pan for 2 minutes per side until the fish is cooked through and flakes easily with a fork.

3. Separate the fish into bite-sized pieces and keep it warm while you **WRAP** the tortillas in damp paper towels and **HEAT** them for 1 minute in the microwave. Serve the tacos with pieces of fish garnished with shredded lettuce, cilantro leaves, chopped tomatoes, or nonfat sour cream.

NUTRITIONAL VALUE PER SERVING			
Calories	210	Total Fat	6g
Carbohydrates	13g	Saturated Fat	0.5g
Protein	25g	Cholesterol	40mg
Fiber	0g	Sodium	190mg
Exchanges: 1 carbohydrate, 3 very lean meats, 1 fat			
Carb Choices: 1			

sole amandine

It's easy to make your own almond flour— all you need is a blender or processor

Serves: 4

Prep Time: 10 minutes

Cooking Time: 15 minutes

INGREDIENTS

4 flounder fillets (about 1 pound)

3/4 teaspoon salt

1/2 cup slivered almonds, toasted (plus a few extra nuts for garnish)

1/2 cup flour

1/8 teaspoon paprika

1/8 teaspoon black pepper

2 egg whites, beaten

1/4 cup water

Cooking spray

2 teaspoons butter

1/4 cup white wine

1 cup milk

1/2 cup low-sodium chicken broth

1/2 teaspoon Worcestershire sauce

1-2 lemons

1. **PREHEAT** oven to 450°F. **RINSE** the fish and remove any bones. If the fish is thicker than 1/4 inch in any part, put it between two pieces of wax paper and gently flatten with a skillet or mallet. **SEASON** the fish with 1/4 teaspoon salt.

2. **COMBINE** the almonds, flour, 1/2 teaspoon salt, paprika, and pepper in a blender or food processor. Pulse to grind the nuts and mix the other ingredients. **POUR** the almond flour into a shallow dish, reserving 2 tablespoons for later. **MIX** the egg whites and water in another shallow dish.

3. **DIP** the fish in the egg wash, then coat in the almond flour. Lay the fish on a foil-covered baking sheet that has been coated with cooking spray. **SPRAY** the breaded fish with cooking spray and set aside.

4. In a small saucepan, **MELT** the butter over medium heat. Add 2 tablespoons of the leftover almond flour. Stir the almond flour and butter for 1 minute. Stir in the white wine and **COOK** 2 more minutes. Add the milk, stock, and Worcestershire sauce. **SIMMER** until the sauce has thickened. Taste and add salt if necessary.

5. **BAKE** the breaded fish 6 minutes, then flip it and bake another 6 minutes until the fish easily flakes with a fork. Squeeze fresh lemon over the fish. **POUR** a neat line of sauce across the middle of the fish. Garnish with leftover toasted almonds and serve.

NUTRITIONAL VALUE PER SERVING			
Calories	330	Total Fat	14g
Carbohydrates	21g	Saturated Fat	3.5g
Protein	28g	Cholesterol	65mg
Fiber	2g	Sodium	600mg

Exchanges: 1 1/2 carbohydrates, 3 extra-lean meats, 2 fats
Carb Choices: 1 1/2

oven-fried cornmeal catfish

Down-home flavor comes with a fraction of the fat of the original recipe

Serves: 4

Prep Time: 15 minutes

Cooking Time: 7 minutes

INGREDIENTS

1¼ pound catfish fillets

1 teaspoon salt

2 egg whites, beaten

¼ cup milk

½ cup cornmeal

½ teaspoon black pepper

Cooking spray

1-2 lemons

1. **PREHEAT** oven to 450°F.

2. **RINSE** fish and inspect for any bones to remove. Dry the fish with paper towels and season lightly with salt on both sides.

3. **COMBINE** egg whites, milk, and ¼ teaspoon salt in a shallow dish. Combine cornmeal, the remaining salt, and black pepper in another shallow dish.

4. Lay a piece of aluminum foil over the preheated baking sheet for easy cleanup. **COAT** the foil-covered baking sheet with cooking spray. **DIP** the seasoned fish in the egg mixture. Shake off any excess and coat in the cornmeal. Arrange the fish on the baking sheet and coat it with cooking spray.

5. **BAKE** 4 minutes. Flip it and bake an additional 2 to 3 minutes, until the fish is cooked through. The fish should be moist and flake easily. **SQUEEZE** lemon juice over the cooked fish and garnish with lemon wedges. Serve immediately with tartar or cocktail sauce.

NUTRITIONAL VALUE PER SERVING			
Calories	270	Total Fat	12g
Carbohydrates	14g	Saturated Fat	3g
Protein	26g	Cholesterol	70mg
Fiber	1g	Sodium	700mg

Exchanges: 1 carbohydrate, 4 lean meats
Carb Choices: 1

steamed seafood and veggie basket

It doesn't get any better than this—a superfast, supernutritional meal, all in one dish

Serves: 4

Prep Time: 15 minutes

Cooking Time: 10 minutes

INGREDIENTS

2 cups broccoli florets

1 carrot, peeled and sliced thinly at an angle

1 cup mushrooms, sliced (1/2-inch thick)

1 cup yellow squash, sliced (1/4-inch thick at an angle)

3/4 pound medium shrimp, peeled and deveined

1/2 pound sea scallops (about **8** large)

1/2 teaspoon salt

1 lemon, in quarters

1 recipe garlic butter sauce (see recipe)

GARLIC BUTTER SAUCE

2 cloves garlic, chopped

2 tablespoons butter or margarine

1 tablespoon shallot, minced

1 cup low-sodium chicken broth

1/2 teaspoon cornstarch

1. In a large steamer basket or 4 individual steamers, LAYER the broccoli, carrot, mushrooms, and squash. TOP with the shrimp and scallops and salt. Set the steamer over a pot of gently boiling water. Cover and STEAM 10 minutes.

2. Carefully remove the steamer from the pot. SQUEEZE fresh lemon over the seafood. Serve with garlic butter sauce and good French bread or Asian soy sesame sauce (see page 81) and steamed rice.

GARLIC BUTTER SAUCE
Serves: 8   Prep Time: 5 minutes

1. HEAT a saucepan over medium heat. Add the garlic, 1 teaspoon butter, and shallot. COOK until the garlic is soft. MIX the broth and cornstarch and add to the pan. Let the sauce come to a boil, then SIMMER until it has thickened slightly and has reduced by a quarter.

2. CUT the remaining butter into small pieces and WHISK each into the sauce, one at a time, and serve. Do not boil the sauce after this point.

Steamed seafood and veggie basket NUTRITIONAL VALUE PER SERVING			
Calories	210	Total Fat	8g
Carbohydrates	9g	Saturated Fat	4g
Protein	25g	Cholesterol	155mg
Fiber	2g	Sodium	510mg

Exchanges: 2 vegetables, 3 very lean meats, 1 1/2 fats
Carb Choices: 1/2

what do I do now?

If I'm watching cholesterol, should I cut seafood out of my diet?

Most nutritionists recommend limiting your cholesterol intake to less than 300 mg per day. Seafood is actually pretty low in cholesterol compared to other animal proteins, except when you're talking about shrimp. Shrimp has about twice the cholesterol of lean chicken or beef but not as much as an egg yolk. Here's a breakdown of calories, fat, protein, and cholesterol in a 3.5-ounce portion of common seafoods compared to other proteins:

Food	Calories	Protein	Fat	Cholesterol
1 egg yolk	60.8	2.8 g	5.2 g	217.8 mg
lean beef	170	28.7 g	5.3 g	81 mg
chicken breast	165	31 g	3.6 g	85 mg
shrimp	99	20.9 g	1.1 g	195 mg
flounder	117	28.2 g	1.5 g	68 mg
trout	169	24 g	7 g	68 mg
lobster	98	20.5 g	.6 g	72 mg
scallops	88	16.8 g	.8 g	33 mg

Figures come from the USDA's National Nutrient Database for Standard Reference

Garlic butter sauce by itself NUTRITIONAL VALUE PER TABLESPOON			
Calories	15	Total Fat	1.5g
Carbohydrates	0g	Saturated Fat	1g
Protein	0g	Cholesterol	5mg
Fiber	0g	Sodium	5mg

Exchanges: 0
Carb Choices: 0

shrimp Louis

Succulent shrimp and tangy dressing make this a scrumptious meal for special friends

Serves: 4

Prep Time: 15 minutes

INGREDIENTS

1/4 cup nonfat mayonnaise

1 tablespoon white wine vinegar or fresh lemon juice

1 tablespoon Worcestershire sauce

1 teaspoon horseradish

1/2 teaspoon hot sauce or chili sauce

1/4 teaspoon salt

1/4 teaspoon fresh black pepper

1 1/2 pounds cooked shrimp

1 stalk celery, diced small

1 tablespoon fresh parsley, chopped

2 green onions, chopped

FOR THE SALAD

4 cups chopped romaine lettuce or mixed greens

1 hardboiled egg

Cherry or grape tomatoes

Green onion or chives

1. In a large bowl, COMBINE the mayonnaise, vinegar, Worcestershire sauce, horseradish, hot sauce, salt, and pepper. MIX well. ADD the shrimp, celery, parsley and onion. MIX gently but thoroughly. CHILL about half an hour before serving.

2. ARRANGE a bed of lettuce on four chilled plates. MOUND 1/4 of the shrimp mixture in the middle of each plate. GRATE 1/4 of the egg over each salad as garnish. GARNISH with cherry or grape tomatoes and slivers of green onion or chives. You can also serve shrimp Louis sandwiches on toasted French or sourdough bread with a green salad on the side.

NUTRITIONAL VALUE PER SERVING			
Calories	220	Total Fat	4g
Carbohydrates	6g	Saturated Fat	1g
Protein	38g	Cholesterol	385mg
Fiber	2g	Sodium	730mg

Exchanges: 1 vegetable, 5 very lean meats
Carb Choices: 1/2

Here's an easy, elegant "spa" meal that you can
prepare in mintues.

sweet and savory roasted salmon

The exotic combo of orange, cinnamon, and spice works well with salmon

Serves: 4

Prep Time: 5 minutes

Cooking Time: 20 minutes

Marinating Time: 60 minutes

INGREDIENTS

1 pound salmon fillet, cut in 4 equal parts

½ cup orange juice

2 tablespoons lime juice

1 tablespoon chili powder

2 teaspoons Splenda

1 teaspoon ground cumin

½ teaspoon salt

¼ teaspoon ground cinnamon

½ red onion, thinly sliced in rings

Cooking spray

1. Rinse the fish well. COMBINE orange and lime juices in a zip-top bag. ADD the fish and MARINATE at least 1 hour.

2. PREHEAT oven to 400°F. Remove the fish from the marinade and discard the marinade. COMBINE the chili powder, Splenda, cumin, salt, and cinnamon. Rub the fish thoroughly with this spice mixture. Arrange the fish skin-side down on a roasting pan or in an oven-safe skillet. TOP with the red onion slices and coat with cooking spray.

3. ROAST for 15 to 20 minutes. When cooked, the fish should flake easily with a fork. Garnish with chopped cilantro and a wedge of lime and serve.

NUTRITIONAL VALUE PER SERVING

Calories	150	Total Fat	4.5g
Carbohydrates	4g	Saturated Fat	1g
Protein	23g	Cholesterol	55mg
Fiber	1g	Sodium	370mg

Exchanges: 3 lean meats
Carb Choices: 0

*The sweet and savory seasoning turns ordinary salmon
into an exceptional dish. Serve with Simmered Yellow
Squash, see page 166.*

shrimp and mushroom scampi

Sure to become a family favorite, this simple dish cooks in just a few minutes

Serves: 4

Prep Time: 5-15 minutes

Cooking Time: 5 minutes

INGREDIENTS

1 pound medium shrimp, peeled and deveined

2 tablespoons olive oil

1/2 teaspoon salt

1/2 teaspoon Splenda

1/2 pound white mushrooms, thinly sliced

2 cloves garlic, thinly sliced

3 tablespoons lemon juice

2 tablespoons bread crumbs, preferably homemade

3 cups linguine or rice, cooked

1. PREHEAT broiler. Raise the rack inside the broiler to the highest position so it's close to the heat source. Have all your ingredients ready to go because this dish cooks very quickly! **RINSE** the shrimp well and pat dry with paper towels. In a bowl, sprinkle 1 tablespoon olive oil, 1/4 teaspoon salt, and the sweetener over the shrimp. **TOSS** to coat well.

2. POUR the remaining olive oil into a heavy, oven-proof pan. **ADD** the mushrooms and toss to coat. Add the shrimp. Spread the shrimp and mushrooms around the pan as evenly as possible. **COOK** under the broiler for 1 1/2 minutes.

3. Carefully and quickly, **ADD** to the pan the garlic, lemon juice, bread crumbs, and remaining salt. **STIR** thoroughly. Return to the broiler and **COOK** 1 1/2 minutes longer. When done, the shrimp should be pink and curled at the edges. The mushrooms should be cooked but not soggy. Serve over linguine or rice.

NUTRITIONAL VALUE PER SERVING			
Calories	360	Total Fat	10g
Carbohydrates	37g	Saturated Fat	1.5g
Protein	30g	Cholesterol	170mg
Fiber	3g	Sodium	490mg

Exchanges: 2 1/2 carbohydrates, 1/2 vegetable, 3 very lean meats, 1 1/2 fats
Carb Choices: 2 1/2

Asian-style steamed fish

A whole fish makes an impressive presentation for family and friends

Serves: 4

Prep Time: 6 minutes

Cooking Time: 20 minutes

Marinating Time: 15 minutes

INGREDIENTS

1 2-pound whole fish (such as snapper, sea bass, or trout), cleaned and scaled

1/4 teaspoon salt

8 green onions

1 2-inch piece of ginger, sliced into thin strips

2 tablespoons dry white wine or dry sherry

1 tablespoon soy sauce

1 tablespoon canola oil

1. **RINSE** the fish in cold water and wipe dry. With a sharp knife, **CUT** 3 or 4 deep diagonal slashes along the length of the fish. The slashes should be about 2 inches long. Rub salt all over the fish and inside the cavity too. **LAY** the fish slash-side up on a heat-proof plate.

2. **TRIM** the roots off the onions. Cut them in thirds. Stack the onion sections together and **SLICE** them into very thin strips lengthwise.

3. Lay about 1/3 of the onion and ginger strips in the cavity of the fish. **SPRINKLE** a little of the wine (or sherry) and soy sauce in the cavity as well. **FILL** each of the slashes with several onion and ginger strips. Sprinkle the top with the remaining soy sauce and sherry. Let marinate for 15 minutes at room temperature.

4. Lay the fish plate in a steamer basket over boiling water. **COVER** with a lid and **STEAM** 16 to 20 minutes. When cooked, the fish should flake easily with a fork. Wear oven mitts when testing the fish and removing it from the steamer; steam burns are extremely painful! **DRAIN** off any of the cloudy liquid that has collected in the fish plate. Keep warm.

5. In a small skillet, **HEAT** the canola oil over medium heat until the oil looks like it's swirling. Carefully **POUR** the hot oil over the fish. Wear oven mitts in case the oil pops or splashes. Transfer carefully to a serving platter. Serve with steamed rice and vegetables.

NUTRITIONAL VALUE PER SERVING			
Calories	130	Total Fat	4.5g
Carbohydrates	3g	Saturated Fat	0g
Protein	17g	Cholesterol	30mg
Fiber	0g	Sodium	440mg

Exchanges: 3 very lean meats, 1/2 fat
Carb Choices: 0

all about fish

How do I know if I'm getting fresh seafood?

Fish should smell pleasantly salty and should never smell fishy or like ammonia. If you are buying a whole fish, it should have bright, clear eyes; feel firm; spring back when pressed; be red or pink at the gills; and have tightly fitting scales that aren't flaking.

Mussels, clams, and oysters should not smell fishy. They should have whole, unchipped shells that are either tightly closed, or close when touched.

Shrimp should not smell fishy. It should feel firm and not slimy and have tightly fitting shells. There should be no black spots on the shell or meat.

Scallops should have a mildly sweet odor and never smell fishy. Look for firm and plump scallops; make sure they are not sitting in lots of excess liquid.

If my grocery store doesn't carry the fish I'm looking for, what should I do?

If you're not used to cooking fish, substitutions can be a little daunting. But fish is very versatile and many are interchangeable. The important things to consider are texture and oil content. Delicate fish might fall apart if you try to grill it. If you do grill it, use a hinged wire basket to prevent it from falling apart. Dense fish, rich in natural oils, are best grilled, roasted, and, in some cases, poached. Here is a quick guide to the most commonly available fish:

BASS This confusing category includes completely unrelated species of freshwater and saltwater fish. In general, the flesh is firm with a mild, slightly sweet flavor. Bass range from lean to moderate in fat content. Grouper, black sea bass, and striped are among the most common kinds. All are suitable for most cooking techniques.

CATFISH A lean, freshwater fish with firm flesh and a delicate flavor. Farm-raised catfish are mild, while wild catfish have a stronger flavor. It's most popularly dredged in cornmeal and fried (or oven-fried), but it can be steamed, baked or grilled, or used in soups and stews.

COD A firm, lean fish with white, delicately flavored meat. Haddock, hake, whiting, and pollack are all related to the cod. Cod is well suited to most cooking techniques.

FLOUNDER Flounder has lean, delicate flesh that flakes easily. It is usually found in fillets. It is mild-flavored and is great oven-fried, baked, steamed, broiled, or poached.

HALIBUT This fish has a low-fat, firm flesh with a mild flavor. Halibut is usually sold in fillets and steaks. It's suitable for many cooking techniques from roasting and baking to steaming and sautéing.

SALMON This favorite has a rich flavor and soft flesh that flakes when cooked. Salmon has a high concentration of "good" fat that is considered important to a heart-healthy diet. Salmon is sold whole or in fillets or steaks. It is often grilled, baked, or poached, served warm or cold. Smoking and curing are also tasty preparations.

SNAPPER With fairly firm flesh, red snapper is the most popular variety. It's suited to any cooking technique and can be used in almost any fish recipe.

TILAPIA With its slightly sweet taste and delicate texture, this fish has recently become very popular in America. It's suitable for baking, broiling, grilling, and steaming.

TROUT Firm-textured and relatively low in fat, rainbow, speckled, and brook trout are the most popular varieties. Trout is typically fried, but is also good baked, grilled, broiled, or stuffed whole and baked.

TUNA A firm fish with a moderate to high fat content, tuna becomes very flaky when cooked. Tuna is usually sold as steaks but comes in fillets too. Tuna is best grilled, broiled, baked, or pan-fried.

Vegetables
Main and Side Dishes

The trick to delectable vegetables is pairing them with complementary flavors—for example, Roasted Sprouts and Cauliflower (page 170) and Simmered Yellow Squash (with onions, page 166). Don't forget you can also turn vegetable dishes into main meals; Just add a carbohydrate, such as pasta or couscous. Consider these two tempting main dishes: Moroccan Veggie Stew with Couscous (top) and Stuffed Peppers (right).

vegetarian country crock

With a salad and corn bread,
this is country cooking at its best

Serves: 4

Prep Time: 10 minutes

Cooking Time: 35 minutes

INGREDIENTS

4 cups water

1 boullion cube (chicken, ham, or vegetarian)

2 cloves garlic, peeled

2 bay leaves

3 medium white potatoes, peeled and cut into eighths

1 large yellow onion, cut into quarters

1 10-ounce package frozen green beans (or $^3/_4$ pound fresh)

$^1/_2$ head of a large white or green cabbage (or a whole small), hard core removed and cut into quarters

$^1/_2$-**1** teaspoon salt

$^1/_2$ teaspoon pepper

1. In a large pot, COMBINE water, boullion cube, garlic, and bay leaves. Bring to a boil. ADD the potatoes, onion, and the green beans if you're using fresh ones. Gently BOIL 10 minutes.

2. Add the frozen green beans and the cabbage. Gently BOIL 15 minutes longer. TEST potatoes for doneness. Taste and add salt and pepper as needed.

3. TRANSFER to serving bowls with plenty of the broth and serve sprinkled generously with chopped parsley, if desired.

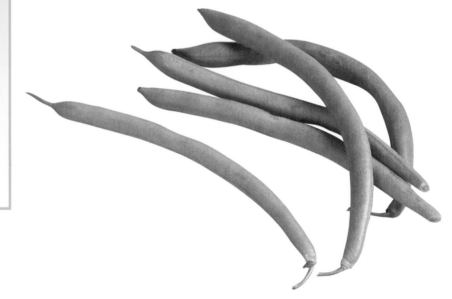

NUTRITIONAL VALUE PER SERVING			
Calories	170	Total Fat	1g
Carbohydrates	39g	Saturated Fat	0g
Protein	6g	Cholesterol	0mg
Fiber	8g	Sodium	750mg
Exchanges: 1 carbohydrate, 3 vegetables			
Carb Choices: 2½			

what do I do now?

Should I use fresh or dried herbs?

The flavor and perfume of fresh herbs can't be beat, but dried herbs are perfectly good substitutes; they also last longer than fresh. Because dried herbs are stronger in flavor than fresh, be sure to halve the amount of dried herbs for fresh. Remember that although dried herbs last longer than fresh, they do lose their flavor after a while. Try to use your dried herbs and spices within six months of purchase.

What's the best way to wash my mushrooms?

Mushrooms are very spongy and absorb water, which dilutes their flavor. Never submerge fresh mushrooms in water to clean them. Small mushrooms with tightly closed caps can be rinsed quickly under running water. But large mushrooms that have lots of dark "gills" under their caps are best wiped clean with a damp paper towel.

How can I chop onions without tearing up?

There are lots of theories on the best way to avoid onion-induced tears. Some cooks suggest wearing sunglasses to keep sulfur-based chemicals in the onion's cells away from your eyes. Others swear that refrigerating your onions causes these irritating substances to make their way more slowly into the air, giving your eyes a short reprieve. The fact is these obnoxious chemicals are part of the onion's charm and they're not going away. The best way to get the job done without crying is to do it quickly (but safely). A very sharp knife and efficient cutting techniques will help speed things along. Peel the onion and cut it in half lengthwise. Lay the onion flat side down. Hold the onion down with the palm of your hand, fingers extended straight. Make one or two horizontal cuts, holding your knife parallel to the cutting board. Don't cut all the way through. Then slice the onion lengthwise vertically, again not cutting all the way through. Now slice the onion as you would normally. You'll have perfectly diced onions in a flash, with hardly a tear in sight. Here's another tip: If you burn a candle near your work area, tears are minimized!

stuffed peppers

Red peppers filled with pasta and mushrooms are a treat for the eye and the palate

Serves: 4

Prep Time: 15 minutes

Cooking Time: 40 minutes

INGREDIENTS

2 large red or yellow bell peppers (green may be substituted)

1 cup orzo pasta or any small pasta

1/4 yellow onion, finely chopped

2 cups mushrooms, chopped

1 cup carrot, grated

1 cup firm silken tofu, cut in small 1/2-inch cubes, or **1** cup cooked chicken, cut into small cubes

3 cloves garlic, minced

1/2 teaspoon dried basil

1/2 teaspoon dried thyme

1/2 teaspoon dried oregano

3/4 -1 cup water

1/2 cup tomato sauce

1/2 teaspoon salt

3 tablespoons Parmesan or low-fat mozzarella cheese, grated

Cooking spray

1. **PREHEAT** the oven to 450°F. **CUT** the peppers in half lengthwise. Remove the seeds and white ribs. **ROAST** the pepper halves on a baking sheet for 10 to 15 minutes, until softened and slightly browned.

2. While the pepper halves cook, **HEAT** a large skillet over medium high. Coat with cooking spray. Add the uncooked pasta and **BROWN** the pasta, stirring often, about 3 minutes. Add the onions, mushrooms, carrots, tofu, garlic, basil, thyme, and oregano. **COOK**, stirring often, about 5 minutes, until the vegetables are very soft.

3. **ADD** the water, tomato sauce, and salt. **STIR** well and let gently boil (higher than a simmer) until the liquid has been absorbed and the pasta is cooked, about 8 minutes.

4. **STIR** in the Parmesan cheese. Taste and adjust the seasoning as needed. **ADD** a little more water if the filling seems very dry.

5. When the peppers are ready, **REDUCE** the oven temperature to 375°F. Sprinkle the peppers with a little salt. **FILL** the pepper halves with the pasta filling. Coat lightly with cooking spray. **BAKE** for 20 minutes until the tops are browned. Serve warm with a fresh salad.

NUTRITIONAL VALUE PER SERVING			
Calories	300	Total Fat	4g
Carbohydrates	52g	Saturated Fat	1g
Protein	15g	Cholesterol	5mg
Fiber	5g	Sodium	580mg

Exchanges: 2½ carbohydrates, 3 vegetables, 1 medium-fat meat
Carb Choices: 1

*Here's a nourishing meal that is as pretty as it is healthful. If you want,
substitute cooked chicken for the tofu. Serve with a tossed salad and
Healthy Ranch Vinaigrette (see page 72).*

hoppin' John

This country classic is a good accompaniment to baked chicken

Serves: 3-4

Prep Time: 5 minutes

Cooking Time: 40 minutes

INGREDIENTS

2 teaspoons olive oil

2 teaspoons margarine

¼ cup onion, chopped

¼ cup green pepper, chopped

⅔ cup long-grain rice, uncooked

1 bay leaf

1 garlic clove, minced

¼ teaspoon dried thyme

1⅓ cup water or low-sodium chicken broth

½ teaspoon salt

1 15-ounce can of black-eyed peas, drained and rinsed

1. **HEAT** a lidded saucepan over medium-high heat. **ADD** the oil and margarine. Add the onion and green pepper, and sauté until the vegetables are softened and the onion is translucent, about 5 minutes.

2. **ADD** the uncooked rice, bay leaf, garlic, and thyme. Stir well. **COOK** for about 5 minutes.

3. **ADD** the water or broth, salt, and black-eyed peas. **BRING** to a boil. Reduce the heat to medium-low and cover. **COOK** 25 to 30 minutes, until the rice is cooked and the liquid is absorbed.

4. **COVER** and let rest 5 minutes. Sprinkle with black pepper and red pepper flakes for a spicier dish. Fluff the hoppin' John with a fork. Taste and adjust the seasoning if necessary.

NUTRITIONAL VALUE PER SERVING			
Calories	230	Total Fat	5g
Carbohydrates	40g	Saturated Fat	1g
Protein	7g	Cholesterol	0mg
Fiber	4g	Sodium	420mg

Exchanges: 2½ carbohydrates, 1 very lean meat, 1 fat
Carb Choices: 2½

veggie fajitas

Marinated tofu and colorful vegetable strips make this a vegetarian fiesta

Serves: 4
Prep Time: 10 minutes
Cooking Time: 15 minutes
Marinating Time: 60 minutes

INGREDIENTS

1/4 cup orange juice

2 cloves garlic, diced

1 teaspoon canola oil

1 teaspoon cumin

1 teaspoon dried oregano

12 ounces regular, extra-firm tofu

1/2-1 teaspoon salt

1 medium squash

1 medium yellow onion

1 medium zucchini

1 small green pepper

1 small red pepper

1 teaspoon lime juice

1 teaspoon hot sauce, preferably Mexican

8-12 4-inch corn tortillas

1. MAKE a marinade by combining the orange juice, garlic cloves, oil, cumin, and oregano. CUT the tofu into 2-inch rectangular strips, about 1/2-inch thick. Using paper towels, press out as much extra water as you can. Put the tofu strips in a glass dish and cover with the marinade. MARINATE at least 1 hour in the refrigerator.

2. While the tofu marinates, CUT the vegetables into thin 2-inch long strips and set aside.

3. HEAT a large frying pan over medium-high heat. Coat with cooking spray. Lay the tofu in the pan. Reserve any extra marinade. BROWN the tofu well on all sides, about 5 minutes. Sprinkle with the salt. Remove from the pan and keep warm.

4. COAT the pan with more cooking spray. ADD the vegetables. Use tongs to toss the vegetables as they cook. POUR any reserved tofu marinade over the vegetables. COOK until the edges are browned but the vegetables are still firm. Squeeze lime juice over the vegetables. Return the tofu to the pan. Add the hot sauce and toss to combine, and cook one more minute.

5. WRAP tortillas in damp paper towels and heat on high for 1 minute in the microwave. Fill the warm tortillas with the tofu-veggie mixture and garnish with nonfat sour cream, chopped cilantro, sliced red onion, or chopped tomato.

NUTRITIONAL VALUE PER SERVING			
Calories	240	Total Fat	8g
Carbohydrates	30g	Saturated Fat	1g
Protein	14g	Cholesterol	0mg
Fiber	3g	Sodium	540mg

Exchanges: 1 1/2 carbohydrates, 2 vegetables, 1 medium-fat meat
Carb Choices: 2

braised tofu and mushrooms

The meatiness of the mushrooms and
smoothness of the tofu combine in a bold stew

Serves: 4

Prep Time: 10 minutes

Cooking Time: 35 minutes

Marinating Time: 60 minutes

INGREDIENTS

2 cloves garlic, minced

1 tablespoon dark soy sauce

1 teaspoon ground ginger

1 12-ounce package silken tofu (extra firm)

Cooking spray

2¹/₂ cups assorted mushrooms, diced (white, shiitake, Portobello, or button, canned or fresh)

1 leek, white part only

2 cups low-sodium vegetable or beef broth

1 cup water chestnuts, sliced and drained

1 teaspoon cornstarch, plus **1** tablespoon water

1. In a bowl, **COMBINE** the garlic, dark soy sauce, and ginger. Mix well. **CUT** the tofu into 16 to 20 cubes and transfer the tofu to a bowl. **POUR** the garlic soy marinade over the tofu and **MARINATE** 1 hour.

2. **CLEAN** the leeks and dice into small pieces (see page 69).

3. **HEAT** a wok or large frying pan over medium-high heat. Coat with cooking spray. Add the mushrooms and slightly **BROWN** 2 minutes, stirring occasionally. Add the broth, chestnuts, tofu, and all the marinating liquid. **STIR** gently to prevent breaking the tofu.

4. **REDUCE** heat to medium and **SIMMER** 20 minutes, until the mushrooms have cooked and the sauce has reduced about half. Add the cornstarch and water. **STIR** well. Increase the heat to medium-high just to get the broth boiling more vigorously (this will activate the cornstarch). Reduce heat to medium and **COOK** another 5 to 10 minutes.

NUTRITIONAL VALUE PER SERVING			
Calories	130	Total Fat	2.5g
Carbohydrates	16g	Saturated Fat	0.5g
Protein	11g	Cholesterol	0mg
Fiber	2g	Sodium	330mg

Exchanges: 2 vegetables, 1 medium-fat meat
Carb Choices: 1

what is it  and where do I get it?

SOY SAUCE

Soy sauce is made by boiling fermented soybeans and wheat, and there are many different types. Light soy sauce is very salty, as thin as water, and barely darkens the color of foods it's used in. Dark soy is richer in flavor and color and less salty than light. Tamari is a very dark, thick Japanese soy sauce with a high sodium content. "Lite," or reduced-sodium, soy sauce is available as well, but it has less flavor. Here's a break-down of sodium in a few soy sauces:

SOY SAUCE	SODIUM PER TABLESPOON
Light	914 mg
Dark	500 mg
Lite	575 mg
Tamari	1,005 mg

TOFU

This low-fat, high-protein food is made from soybeans. Tofu comes in many different styles: soft, firm, extra-firm, and hard. Firm tofu is easy to stir-fry, pan-fry, or grill. Soft tofu is better suited to purees and gentle cooking methods. Besides the soft/firm distinction, Chinese-style tofu is generally called "regular" tofu, while "silken" tofu refers to the Japanese style. Silken is softer and has a finer texture than regular. Both varieties have very little flavor on their own but do well when combined with bold ingredients. Here are some tips for cooking with tofu:

■ If at all possible, marinate your tofu for an hour or more before cooking.

■ Make a tofu press to get rid of water in the tofu and create a firmer texture. Cut the tofu into 1/2-inch slices. Lay the slices on a plate with several layers of paper towel. Cover the tofu with more paper towels and place another plate on top. Weight the plate with a few jars or cans. Chill the tofu press for at least an hour, changing the paper towels once. This works for silken or regular tofu.

Moroccan veggie stew with couscous

Roasting vegetables brings out their bold sweetness—a perfect match for nutty chickpeas and couscous

Serves: 4

Prep Time: 10 minutes

Cooking Time: 50 minutes

INGREDIENTS

2 carrots, peeled and cut into 1-inch segments

2 cloves garlic, diced

1 large yellow onion, peeled and cut into 1-inch pieces

Cooking spray

1/4 teaspoon salt

1 cup dry couscous

2 1/2 cups low-sodium vegetable or chicken broth

1 8-ounce jar roasted red peppers, drained and chopped

1 15-ounce can diced tomatoes, drained

1 15-ounce can chickpeas, drained

1 bay leaf

1/2 teaspoon ground cinnamon

1/4 teaspoon black pepper

1 teaspoon creamy peanut butter

1. **PREHEAT** oven to 400°F. Arrange the carrots, garlic, and onion on a roasting pan. Lightly coat with cooking spray and sprinkle with 1/4 teaspoon of salt. **ROAST** for 30 minutes, until the vegetables have browned nicely.

2. While the vegetables bake, make the couscous. **POUR** the couscous into a large bowl. Bring 2 cups of broth to a boil. Pour the boiling broth over the couscous and **COVER** the bowl tightly with plastic wrap. Let sit 10 minutes, then fluff the couscous with a fork. Set aside.

3. **ADD** the roasted vegetables, peppers, tomatoes, chickpeas, bay leaf, cinnamon, and black pepper in a casserole dish. **MIX** well. Add 1/4 cup broth and return the stew to the oven. Reduce heat to 350°F and **BAKE** 20 minutes.

4. **REMOVE** the bay leaf. In a small bowl, mix the peanut butter with 1/4 cup broth until smooth and **POUR** into the stew. Mix well. Taste and adjust the salt and pepper as needed. To serve, put the couscous on a large, deep serving platter. Make a large well in the middle and **LADLE** the thick stew into the well.

NUTRITIONAL VALUE PER SERVING			
Calories	340	Total Fat	3g
Carbohydrates	64g	Saturated Fat	1g
Protein	14g	Cholesterol	0mg
Fiber	9g	Sodium	740mg

Exchanges: 3 carbohydrates, 3 vegetables, 1 very lean meat
Carb Choices: 4 1/2

what is it  and where do I get it?

COUSCOUS

This North African favorite looks like a grain, but it's actually more like a pasta made from semolina. You can buy it in most large grocery stores in the international food section, or in bulk at health food stores. Couscous is a delicious alternative to rice or other pastas. It is well suited to pilaf and salads. The best part is that couscous "cooks" in about 5 minutes, off the stove, with just the addition of boiling water or broth.

This is a fun alternative to the traditional pasta dinner. Here vegetables and chickpeas, in a succulent tomato sauce, are served over couscous.

sweet potato mash

Sweet potatoes are high in vitamin A and complement grilled or roasted meats

Serves: 4

Prep Time: 8 minutes

Cooking Time: 15-25 minutes

INGREDIENTS

2 large sweet potatoes

1 tablespoon Splenda

3 teaspoons light margarine

1/2 teaspoon salt

1/4 teaspoon black pepper

1. PEEL the sweet potatoes and DICE into 1-inch cubes. Cover with cold water and bring to a boil. BOIL about 15 minutes, until the potatoes are very tender. DRAIN, reserving about 1/2 cup of the boiling liquid.

2. With a potato masher, begin to MASH the sweet potatoes. ADD the Splenda, margarine, salt, and black pepper. Mash thoroughly. ADD some of the reserved boiling liquid to make the mixture smoother, if necessary. Taste and adjust the seasoning. Serve hot.

NUTRITIONAL VALUE PER SERVING			
Calories	110	Total Fat	1.5g
Carbohydrates	22g	Saturated Fat	0g
Protein	2g	Cholesterol	0mg
Fiber	3g	Sodium	330mg

Exchanges: 1 1/2 carbohydrates
Carb Choices: 1 1/2

First Person Disaster:
Portion Control Made Easy

My husband and I are carb addicts! When he developed Type 2 diabetes a few years ago, we started watching our diet more. I reminded him to go easy on the carbs because they affect blood sugar. But it was really hard for him to resist seconds of the starches, and his blood sugar suffered. Our diabetes educator emphasized portion control. So I stopped bringing a big serving bowl of potatoes or pasta to the dinner table and started filling our plates in the kitchen. I measured everything very carefully with measuring cups at first. Then I discovered that an ice cream scoop of mashed potatoes is just the right serving size of mashed potatoes. I found a bowl that measures $1/2$ cup and started using that to make a perfect little mound of rice, just like they serve in restaurants. I put the leftovers in the refrigerator right away so we wouldn't be tempted for seconds. It was tough at first, but my husband got used to the new portion sizes. Our dinner plates look like works of art, and the best part is we're finally controlling our carb intake.

—Maddy B., Trimont, MN

"grate" potato cakes

Here's an alternative to mashed or baked potatoes with no extra fat to weigh them down

Serves: 4

Prep Time: 8 minutes

Cooking Time: 20 minutes

INGREDIENTS

2 medium Yukon gold potatoes, scrubbed well

¼ cup onion, diced small

¼ cup red or green pepper, diced small

2 teaspoons flour

¼ teaspoon salt

Black pepper to taste

Cooking spray

1. **PREHEAT** the oven to 375°F. On a box grater, **GRATE** the potatoes, skin and all. Take a handful of grated potato and squeeze out as much water as you can. Place the squeezed potato in a separate bowl. **REPEAT** with the rest of the grated potato.

2. **ADD** the onion, peppers, and flour to the grated potato. **MIX** thoroughly.

3. With very clean hands, **FORM** 8 thin potato patties. Press them firmly between your palms.

4. **LAY** the potato cakes on a baking sheet coated with cooking spray. **BAKE** 10 minutes on each side. Season with salt and pepper after the cakes are cooked. Serve warm.

NUTRITIONAL VALUE PER SERVING			
Calories	110	Total Fat	0g
Carbohydrates	24g	Saturated Fat	0g
Protein	2g	Cholesterol	0mg
Fiber	2g	Sodium	150mg

Exchanges: 1 1/2 carbohydrates
Carb Choices: 1 1/2

what do I do now?

Does it matter which potatoes I use?

Some potatoes are better suited to certain cooking techniques than others. The starchier, "mealier" potatoes, like baking potatoes and russets (also called Idaho potatoes), are best suited to baking, mashing, and roasting.

Waxy potatoes, such as Red Bliss, and all types of new potatoes have more moisture and less starch than baking potatoes. Waxy potatoes are best suited for boiling, roasting, and baking in casseroles because they hold their shape nicely.

Yukon golds and white potatoes fall between waxy potatoes and baking potatoes in starch and moisture content and work well in any potato preparation. Here's a breakdown of the carbohydrate, calorie, and fiber content of one small potato (138 g) in each category.

Potato	Calories	Carbohydrate	Fiber
Waxy (red)	123	27 g	2.8 g
White	130	29 g	2.9 g
Baking (russet)	134	30 g	3.2 g

Figures come from the USDA's National Nutrient Database for Standard Reference

spicy garlic green beans

Roasting green beans concentrates their flavors while keeping them tender-crisp

Serves: 4

Prep Time: 6 minutes

Cooking Time: 10-12 minutes

INGREDIENTS

3/4 pound fresh green beans (try a mix of fresh wax beans and green beans)

2 cloves garlic, chopped

1 teaspoon canola oil

1/4 teaspoon salt

1/4 teaspoon pepper

1/8 teaspoon red pepper flakes

1. **PREHEAT** oven to 400°F. **TRIM** tough end off the beans. Leave them whole. **RINSE** well and shake dry.

2. Put the beans, garlic, oil, salt, and black pepper in a large zip-top plastic bag. **ROLL** the bag between your palms to coat the beans with garlic and oil. Lay the beans in a single layer on a baking sheet. Sprinkle with the red pepper flakes. **ROAST** 6 minutes, then stir to redistribute. **COOK** another 4 to 5 minutes, until the beans are browned in spots. The skin should look a little cracked, but the beans should be tender-crisp. Serve warm.

what do I do now?

How can I avoid overcooking the garlic?

Garlic can zip up any dish, adding flavor and aroma, and this powerful ingredient can be tamed in a number of ways. If you cook a whole garlic clove, you'll experience a very mild garlic flavor and aroma in the rest of your dish. The garlic clove will become tender and sweet with a gentle flavor. Dicing garlic produces a stronger garlic taste and a little more "heat." The smaller you chop it, the more pungent it becomes since more acids and enzymes are released. Slicing garlic produces a less strong flavor than mincing. Finely chopped garlic burns quickly and becomes bitter, so avoid doing this. Smashing garlic into a paste is a good way to get a lot of flavor for even distribution in a sauce or marinade. Remember, a little smashed garlic goes a long way.

NUTRITIONAL VALUE PER SERVING

Calories	40	Total Fat	1.5g
Carbohydrates	6g	Saturated Fat	0g
Protein	2g	Cholesterol	0mg
Fiber	2g	Sodium	150mg

Exchanges: 1 vegetable
Carb Choices: 1/2

roasted balsamic tomatoes

A great, easy side dish to throw in the oven while you're cooking the main course

Serves: 4

Prep Time: 6 minutes

Cooking Time: 12 minutes

INGREDIENTS

6 ripe Roma tomatoes

1 teaspoon balsamic vinegar

1/2 teaspoon salt

2 tablespoons bread crumbs

1 tablespoon Parmesan cheese, grated

1. PREHEAT oven to 400°F. Cut a small slice off the ends of each tomato to make flat surfaces so the tomatoes will sit flat. **CUT** each tomato in half horizontally.

2. Arrange the tomato halves on their flattened ends, wider cut side up, in a small roasting dish or heavy pie pan. **SPRINKLE** a few drops of balsamic vinegar, and salt on each tomato half.

3. MIX the bread crumbs and cheese together in a bowl. Sprinkle 3/4 teaspoon of the mixture on each tomato half. **BAKE** 10 to 12 minutes until the tomatoes are softened, releasing some of their juices, and the crumb topping is browned. Serve warm.

what is it and where do I get it?

ROMA TOMATOES

Romas are members of the Italian plum tomato family. They are small, oval-shaped tomatoes with firm flesh, few seeds, and a deliciously fruity flavor. They are readily available in groceries and are often of better quality than regular tomatoes during winter and spring months, when tomatoes are out of season.

NUTRITIONAL VALUE PER SERVING			
Calories	40	Total Fat	1g
Carbohydrates	7g	Saturated Fat	0g
Protein	2g	Cholesterol	0mg
Fiber	1g	Sodium	350mg

Exchanges: 1 vegetable
Carb Choices: 1/2

simmered yellow squash

Simmering onion and squash together enhances the flavor of both vegetables

Serves: 4

Prep Time: 5 minutes

Cooking Time: 20 minutes

INGREDIENTS

3 medium yellow squash, cut in ½-inch slices

1 small onion, cut in ½-inch slices

3/4 cup water

1/4 teaspoon salt

Black pepper to taste

1. **COMBINE** the squash, onion, and water in a lidded saucepan over medium-high heat. Bring the water to a gentle boil.

2. **REDUCE** heat to medium and cover. **SIMMER** 15 to 20 minutes, stirring occasionally, until the squash is very tender. **SEASON** with salt and pepper. Serve hot.

So easy to make, so fresh and flavorful!

garlicky mustard greens

The slight bitterness of the greens and the kick of garlic make this a perfect side dish

Serves: 4

Prep Time: 6 minutes

Cooking Time: 6-7 minutes

INGREDIENTS

1 pound fresh mustard greens, washed (fresh spinach or chard may be substituted)

1 teaspoon canola oil

2 cloves garlic, peeled and sliced thin

1/4 teaspoon salt

2 tablespoons water

1/8 teaspoon black pepper

1. **RIP** the mustard greens in large pieces and remove any tough stems. **RINSE** the greens and shake thoroughly.

2. **HEAT** a wok or large frying pan over high heat. **ADD** the oil. Heap the greens in the hot pan and add the garlic on top of them. Be careful as the oil might pop a little bit. If all the greens don't fit, just let the greens **WILT** down for about 30 seconds and **ADD** the rest on top. Sprinkle with salt to help the wilting.

3. Gently **LIFT** the greens from the bottom, turning them over so the wilted ones come to the top. **ADD** more greens and sprinkle with salt and a tablespoon of water. When all the greens are in the pan, add the remaining tablespoon of water and **TOSS** gently with tongs. Cover the pan and **COOK** 1 to 2 minutes, until the greens are completely wilted and tender, but still bright green. Taste and adjust the seasoning. Serve warm.

Simmered yellow squash NUTRITIONAL VALUE PER SERVING			
Calories	35	Total Fat	0g
Carbohydrates	8g	Saturated Fat	0g
Protein	2g	Cholesterol	0mg
Fiber	3g	Sodium	150mg
Exchanges: 1 1/2 vegetables Carb Choices: 1/2			

Garlicky mustard greens NUTRITIONAL VALUE PER SERVING			
Calories	25	Total Fat	1.5g
Carbohydrates	3g	Saturated Fat	0g
Protein	2g	Cholesterol	0mg
Fiber	2g	Sodium	160mg
Exchanges: 1 vegetable Carb Choices: 0			

quick kale and tomatoes

Steam-sautéing kale creates wonderful texture and body in this hearty dish

Serves: 4

Prep Time: 7 minutes

Cooking Time: 14 minutes

INGREDIENTS

1 pound fresh kale, washed

1½ cups water

½ cup yellow onion, chopped

1 teaspoon olive oil

1 cup tomato, chopped

½ teaspoon balsamic vinegar

¼ teaspoon salt

Dash of black pepper

½-1 cup canned chickpeas, rinsed and drained

1. **REMOVE** the thick stems from the washed kale. With a sharp chef's knife angled down, lightly "chop" downward along the stem to cut the leaf away. **STACK** the leaves and cut into strips.

2. In a large skillet with a lid, bring the water to a boil. **ADD** the kale and cover. Reduce heat to medium-high and **COOK** 5 minutes.

3. **REMOVE** the cover. Most of the water should have evaporated. The kale should be tender and bright green. **ADD** the onion and olive oil and **STIR** well. Add the tomato, balsamic vinegar, salt, and pepper. Stir and **COOK** 3 minutes. **ADD** the chickpeas and toss gently. Taste and adjust the seasoning. Serve warm.

NUTRITIONAL VALUE PER SERVING			
Calories	160	Total Fat	3g
Carbohydrates	29g	Saturated Fat	0g
Protein	7g	Cholesterol	0mg
Fiber	6g	Sodium	380mg

Exchanges: ½ carbohydrate, 3 vegetables, ½ very lean meat
Carb Choices: 2

springy succotash

A little milk added at the end brings extra sweetness to this flavorful mix

Serves: 4

Prep Time: 5 minutes

Cooking Time: 17 minutes

INGREDIENTS

1 teaspoon margarine

1/4 cup yellow onion, chopped

1/4 cup red bell pepper, chopped

2 cups green beans (fresh or frozen, thawed), cut into 1-inch pieces

1 1/2 cups corn kernels (fresh or frozen, thawed)

1/4 cup low-sodium vegetable or chicken broth

1 small clove garlic, minced

1/4 cup milk

1/4 teaspoon salt

1/4 teaspoon black pepper

1. **MELT** the margarine in a skillet over medium-high heat. **ADD** the onion and red pepper. Sauté about 2 minutes, until softened and the onion is translucent.

2. **ADD** the green beans, corn, broth, and garlic. Bring to a boil, then reduce heat to medium and **SIMMER** the vegetables until tender and most of the liquid has evaporated, about 10 minutes.

3. Add the milk and **COOK** another 5 minutes until most of the milk has evaporated too. **SEASON** with salt and pepper and serve.

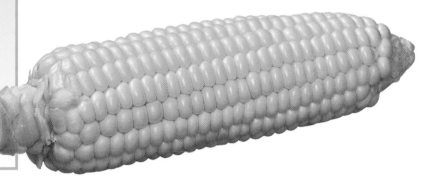

NUTRITIONAL VALUE PER SERVING			
Calories	100	Total Fat	2.5g
Carbohydrates	18g	Saturated Fat	0.5g
Protein	4g	Cholesterol	0mg
Fiber	4g	Sodium	180mg
Exchanges: 1 carbohydrate, 1 vegetable			
Carb Choices: 1			

roasted sprouts and cauliflower

Brussels sprouts and cauliflower explode with flavor and texture when roasted

Serves: 6-8

Prep Time: 5 minutes

Cooking Time: 30 minutes

INGREDIENTS

1 medium cauliflower, quartered, cored and cut into 1-inch florets

2 cups Brussels sprouts, halved lengthwise

1 small yellow onion, coarsely chopped

1 large clove garlic, sliced as thin as possible

2 tablespoons olive oil

½ teaspoon black pepper

¼ teaspoon salt

1. PREHEAT the oven to 350°F. In a large bowl, **COMBINE** cauliflower, Brussels sprouts, onion, and garlic. **ADD** the oil and mix well.

2. SPREAD the vegetables on a large jelly-roll pan. Sprinkle with pepper and salt.

3. ROAST until the vegetables are crisp-tender and browned at edges, about 20 to 30 minutes. Serve warm.

This roasted vegetable side dish is a snap to make and goes beautifully with meats and chicken.

veggie baked potatoes

Fresh vegetables brighten baked potatoes in this steak house side dish

Serves: 4

Prep Time: 8 minutes

Cooking Time: 1 hour 20 minutes

INGREDIENTS

2 medium russet potatoes

1/2 teaspoon salt

2 large cloves garlic, not peeled

2 tablespoons nonfat sour cream

1 tablespoon butter or margarine

1/2 cup frozen peas, thawed

4 large mushrooms, chopped

1 small squash, diced

Cooking spray

1. **PREHEAT** oven to 375°F. **SCRUB** the potatoes under cold water. Dry and poke with a fork a few times. Sprinkle with a little salt. **BAKE** directly on the middle rack of the oven until the skins are crisp but they "give" when you squeeze them, 45 minutes to 1 hour. Wrap the garlic cloves in a piece of foil and **BAKE** them with the potatoes, about 30 minutes, until they are very soft. **REMOVE** the garlic until you're ready to use it.

2. Let the potatoes cool 10 minutes before trying to handle them. **CUT** the potatoes lengthwise. With a spoon, **SCOOP** out the middles of each half into a bowl, leaving a 1/4–inch thick shell. Place the potato "shells" on a baking sheet and return them to the oven while you make the filling.

3. In a small bowl, **MASH** the potato flesh with a fork. Snip the end off each clove of roasted garlic and squeeze the pulp into the potatoes. **ADD** the sour cream, butter, and the remaining salt. **MASH** well. Add the peas, mushrooms, and squash. **MIX** well. Taste and adjust the seasoning as needed.

4. **SPOON** the filling back into the potato shells. Coat lightly with cooking spray. **BAKE** 15 to 20 minutes, until the tops have browned. Serve warm.

Roasted sprouts and cauliflower NUTRITIONAL VALUE PER SERVING			
Calories	60	Total Fat	3.5g
Carbohydrates	7g	Saturated Fat	0.5g
Protein	2g	Cholesterol	0mg
Fiber	3g	Sodium	100mg

Exchanges: 1 1/2 vegetables, 1 1/2 fats
Carb Choices: 1/2

Veggie baked potatoes NUTRITIONAL VALUE PER SERVING			
Calories	150	Total Fat	3g
Carbohydrates	28g	Saturated Fat	2g
Protein	4g	Cholesterol	10mg
Fiber	4g	Sodium	330mg

Exchanges: 1 carbohydrate, 1 vegetable, 1 fat
Carb Choices: 2

Chapter 10

Desserts

Thanks to the wonderful sugar-free substitutes on the market today, people with diabetes can have their cake and eat it too. Try these fabulous desserts: a Simple Trifle (top), and Bananas Foster (right).

mocha mousse pie

With chocolate and coffee whipped to fluffy perfection, this is a pie no one can resist

Serves: 8

Prep Time: 15 minutes

Cooking Time: 8 minutes

Freezing Time: 2 hours

INGREDIENTS

10 graham crackers (2 by 2 inches each)

2 tablespoons butter or margarine

1.5 ounces baking unsweetened chocolate

1 1-ounce box sugar-free, fat-free instant chocolate pudding

2 cups low-fat milk

4 teaspoons instant coffee crystals

1½ cups light whipped topping

1 teaspoon Splenda

1. CRUSH the graham crackers roughly in a blender or food processor. Pulse to crush well. Add the butter and pulse to combine until a sandy texture is reached. Rub the sides of a 9-inch glass pie pan with margarine. POUR the graham cracker mixture into the buttered dish. SPREAD the crumbs evenly over the bottom of the dish and press down firmly to make a bottom crust. Set aside.

2. PLACE a small saucepan filled with 2 inches of water over medium-high heat. Set a clean, dry mixing bowl over the saucepan; the bowl should not touch the simmering water. Put the baking chocolate in the bowl to gently melt, approximately 8 minutes.

3. In a large mixing bowl, COMBINE the pudding mix, milk, and coffee crystals. With a handheld electric mixer, MIX 2 minutes until the pudding has thickened. FOLD in ¾ of the melted chocolate. Gently fold in the whipped topping.

4. POUR the mousse filling into the pie shell and SMOOTH it out. ADD Splenda to the remaining melted chocolate and mix. With a spoon, drizzle the sweetened chocolate in a random pattern over the mousse pie. FREEZE at least 2 hours before serving. If you keep the pie frozen longer, soften it for 15 to 30 minutes at room temperature before serving.

NUTRITIONAL VALUE PER SERVING			
Calories	110	Total Fat	8g
Carbohydrates	11g	Saturated Fat	4.5g
Protein	1g	Cholesterol	15mg
Fiber	1g	Sodium	190mg

Exchanges: 1 carbohydrate, 1 fat
Carb Choices: 1

This low-fat, sugar-free chocolate pie makes a perfect ending to any meal.

the perfect sponge cake

Moist and light, this cake is delicious
on its own or dolled up in dozens of ways

Serves: 8
Prep Time: 25 minutes
Cooking Time: 25 minutes

INGREDIENTS

2 eggs

2 egg whites

1/4 cup Splenda

2 tablespoons sugar

2 tablespoons canola oil

1 teaspoon vanilla extract

3/4 cup all purpose flour, sifted

1/4 teaspoon baking soda

1/2 teaspoon white vinegar

1. **PREHEAT** oven to 350°F. Butter and flour a 9-inch cake pan.

2. Set a saucepan, filled 1/3 with water, on medium-high heat. Set a medium mixing bowl over the saucepan; the bowl should not touch the simmering water. **ADD** the eggs, egg whites, Splenda, and sugar. **WHISK** by hand until the eggs are foamy and slightly warm. Add the oil and, if possible, use an electric mixer to **MIX** the eggs until they are very fluffy and warm to the touch. You can also do this step by hand. **REMOVE** from heat and **ADD** the vanilla.

3. With an electric mixer, **BEAT** until the eggs are tripled in volume and fall in a thick ribbon when the whisk is lifted from the mixture, about 5 minutes. If your mixing bowl is too small, pour the egg mixture into a larger bowl before vigorously beating.

4. With a large rubber spatula, **FOLD** 1/6 of the flour and the baking soda into the whipped egg mixture. Continue folding in the rest of the flour one small portion at a time. Be gentle; you don't want to deflate the eggs you've spent 5 minutes beating.

5. **POUR** the vinegar into the egg mixture and gently fold it in. Pour the batter into the prepared pan. **BAKE** 20 to 25 minutes until golden brown and a toothpick inserted comes out clean. **COOL** 10 minutes before removing the cake from the pan.

6. Serve this cake warm or at room temperature, dusted with powdered sugar and garnished with mint, berries, or sliced toasted nuts. Or use this cake in any number of other recipes calling for a simple vanilla cake.

The perfect sponge cake
NUTRITIONAL VALUE PER SERVING

Calories	110	Total Fat	5g
Carbohydrates	13g	Saturated Fat	0.5g
Protein	4g	Cholesterol	55mg
Fiber	0g	Sodium	70mg

Exchanges: 1 carbohydrate
Carb Choices: 1

VARIATIONS

To make a jam cake: **COMBINE** in a bowl 2 tablespoons of water, 1 tablespoon Splenda and 1 tablespoon of your favorite fruit spread (strawberry or peach are terrific). Poke holes in the hot sponge cake and **POUR** the syrup over. **COOL** the cake completely before removing it from the pan. Cut the cake into two layers with a serrated knife. Spread more fruit spread between the layers and on top. Dust with powdered sugar and **SPRINKLE** with sliced toasted almonds.

To make lemon sponge cake: Just **FOLD** 1 tablespoon of freshly grated lemon zest into the batter and **BAKE**. Mix in a bowl 2 tablespoons of freshly squeezed lemon juice, 2 tablespoons of water, and 2 tablespoons of Splenda. Poke holes all over the hot cake and **POUR** the lemon syrup over the cake. **COOL** the cake completely before removing it from the pan. A dusting of powdered sugar, a dollop of light whipped topping, and a grating of fresh lemon zest make for a beautiful presentation.

what do I do now?

Why is vinegar used in baking?
Vinegar added to the batter at the last minute reacts with baking soda, producing bubbles to make cakes rise. It's an old baking trick from the days when eggs and butter and milk weren't always available.

simple trifle

Layers of fruit, custard, cream, and cake make this a dessert centerpiece

Serves: 8

Prep Time: 25 minutes

Chilling Time: 1 to 24 minutes

INGREDIENTS

4 cups cut fruit, sliced (any berries, peaches, mandarin oranges, kiwi, mango, or pineapple will work well), or **16** ounces of frozen fruit, thawed

3 teaspoons of Splenda

1/2 of a sponge cake or angel food cake

1/4 cup pineapple juice

1 tablespoon Grand Marnier or other fruity liqueur

2 cups cold low-fat milk

1 1-ounce box fat-free, sugar-free instant vanilla pudding

2 cups light whipped topping

1. **TOSS** the fruit with 2 teaspoons of Splenda. Let sit 30 minutes at room temperature to bring out their juices.

2. **CUT** a sponge cake in 1-inch cubes, about 6 cups. In a large bowl, **COMBINE** the pineapple juice, Grand Marnier, and 1 teaspoon Splenda. **ADD** the cake cubes and toss to moisten the cake.

3. **COMBINE** the milk and the pudding mixture and **MIX** according to the package directions.

4. In a large glass bowl or trifle dish, arrange a layer of cake. **TOP** with half the pudding, then one third of the whipped topping, then half the fruit. Repeat the layering, ending with the remaining third of whipped toping. **COVER** with plastic wrap and **CHILL** at least one hour or overnight. Serve garnished with mint or chopped nuts.

NUTRITIONAL VALUE PER SERVING			
Calories	190	Total Fat	3.5g
Carbohydrates	37g	Saturated Fat	1.5g
Protein	5g	Cholesterol	40mg
Fiber	2g	Sodium	260mg

Exchanges: 1½ carbohydrates, 1 fruit, 1 fat
Carb Choices: 2½

Fruit makes a terrific healthy dessert. For a little added pleasure,
combine your fruit with a bit of sugar-free vanilla pudding, low-fat
sponge cake, and light whipped topping.

easy carrot cake with cream cheese frosting

Rich, moist, spiced, and sweet, this cake is the perfect ending to a light dinner

Serves: 8

Prep Time: 20 minutes

Cooking Time: 20-25 minutes

INGREDIENTS

Cooking spray

2 cups carrot, grated (about **3** medium carrots)

1 cup pineapple, crushed

$1/2$ cup coconut, shredded

$1^1/3$ cups flour

$1/2$ teaspoon baking powder

$1/4$ teaspoon baking soda

$1/4$ teaspoon salt

2 eggs

$1/4$ cup oil

$1/4$ cup Splenda

$1/2$ teaspoon cinnamon

$1/4$ teaspoon nutmeg

$1/4$ cup applesauce

$1^1/2$ cups cream cheese frosting (below)

$1/4$ cup walnuts, chopped

CREAM CHEESE FROSTING

$3/4$ cup nonfat cream cheese (6 ounces)

$1/4$ cup milk

$1/4$ cup Splenda (or **3** packets Equal)

2 tablespoons tub-style butter or margarine

1 teaspoon vanilla

1. **PREHEAT** oven to 350°F. **COAT** 2 8-inch cake pans with cooking spray and lay a circle of wax paper in the bottom of each. **COMBINE** the carrots, pineapple, coconut, and $1/3$ cup of flour in a bowl. **TOSS** to coat the carrots and fruits with the flour. This keeps them from sinking in the cake.

2. **SIFT** 1 cup flour, baking powder, baking soda, and salt together.

3. With a handheld electric mixer, **MIX** the eggs, oil, Splenda, cinnamon, and nutmeg. Mix until light and slightly increased in volume. **FOLD** in the applesauce.

4. Gently **MIX** in the flour mixture. Fold in the carrots and fruit by hand. Don't over-mix. **POUR** into the pans. **BAKE** 20 to 25 minutes until a toothpick inserted comes out clean. Turn out on a rack to cool completely.

5. While the cake bakes, make the icing. **SPREAD** the icing over the bottom layer. Sprinkle with half the chopped nuts. Top with the second layer and finish icing the top and sides of the cake. Sprinkle the remaining nuts over the top. **REFRIGERATE** until ready to serve.

CREAM CHEESE FROSTING

Serves: 8   Prep Time: 5 minutes

1. **BEAT** the cream cheese, milk, Splenda and butter with a handheld electric mixer on low until light and very fluffy.

2. **ADD** vanilla and beat until very smooth. Makes $1^1/4$ cups.

what do I do now?

Can I substitute baking soda for baking powder?

If you ever made a "volcano" in elementary school by mixing baking soda and vinegar, you know that seemingly placid baking soda can put on quite a show. When baking soda, a.k.a. bicarbonate of soda, is combined with acidic substances, such as vinegar, lemon juice, sour milk, buttermilk, or molasses, carbon dioxide bubbles form. These bubbles are what make cakes rise. The reaction takes place right away, so always mix the baking soda with the dry ingredients first. Combine them with the acidic ingredients last and get the batter in the oven as soon as possible.

Baking soda plus a dry acidic ingredient, usually cream of tartar, make up baking powder. In a pinch, 1/4 teaspoon of baking soda plus 5/8 teaspoon of cream of tartar can take the place of 1 teaspoon of baking powder.

Just a note about cream of tartar: A little added to egg whites before beating makes them fluffier and more stable, which is most desirable when making meringue.

Easy carrot cake NUTRITIONAL VALUE PER SERVING			
Calories	300	Total Fat	17g
Carbohydrates	29g	Saturated Fat	5g
Protein	8g	Cholesterol	55mg
Fiber	3g	Sodium	320mg
Exchanges: 2 carbohydrates, 3 fats Carb Choices: 2			

Cream cheese frosting by itself NUTRITIONAL VALUE PER TABLESPOON			
Calories	20	Total Fat	1g
Carbohydrates	1g	Saturated Fat	0g
Protein	2g	Cholesterol	0mg
Fiber	0g	Sodium	75mg
Exchanges: 0 Carb Choices: 0			

velvet coconut cupcakes

These fluffy little cakes will melt in your mouth

Makes: 12 cupcakes

Prep Time: 10 minutes

Cooking Time: 12-15 minutes

INGREDIENTS

¹/₄ cup flour

2¹/₂ teaspoons baking powder

1 large egg

³/₄ cup Splenda

¹/₃ cup canola oil

1 teaspoon vanilla

1 teaspoon white vinegar (see page 177)

³/₄ cup coconut milk

¹/₄ cup milk

¹/₂ cup coconut, shredded

1. **PREHEAT** oven to 350°F. Sift together the flour and baking powder and set aside.

2. With a handheld electric mixer, **BEAT** the egg, Splenda, oil, vanilla, and vinegar until the mixture is pale yellow and the batter falls in a ribbon shape when the whisk is lifted.

3. **MIX** in a separate bowl the coconut milk and milk. Add ¹/₃ of the flour mixture to the batter and mix on medium. **MIX** in ¹/₃ of the milk mixture. **ADD** the remaining flour and milk in alternating thirds. Scrape down the sides of the bowl.

4. **POUR** the smooth, shiny batter into 12 paper-lined cupcake tins. Sprinkle each cupcake generously with some shredded coconut. **BAKE** 12 minutes until a toothpick inserted comes out clean.

Velvet coconut cupcakes
NUTRITIONAL VALUE PER CUPCAKE

Calories	130	Total Fat	12g
Carbohydrates	5g	Saturated Fat	6g
Protein	2g	Cholesterol	20mg
Fiber	0g	Sodium	95mg

Exchanges: ¹/₂ carbohydrate, 2¹/₂ fats
Carb Choices: ¹/₂

pumpkin cheesecake

Rich and creamy, and so easy to make, this is sure to become a holiday favorite

Serves: 8

Prep Time: 15 minutes

Cooking Time: 35-40 minutes

Chilling Time: 3 hours

INGREDIENTS

10 graham crackers
(2 by 2 inches each)

1½ tablespoons margarine

Cooking spray

8 ounces low-fat cream cheese, softened

½ cup Splenda

1 teaspoon cinnamon

1 teaspoon vanilla extract

1 cup unsweetened pumpkin puree

3 eggs

2 egg whites

1 cup light whipped topping (optional)

1. In a blender or food processor, coarsely **CRUMBLE** the graham crackers. Pulse to crush them quite fine. **ADD** the margarine and pulse to achieve a sandy consistency. Coat a 9-inch pie pan that's at least 2 inches deep with cooking spray. If you have a 9-inch springform pan, feel free to use that instead. **POUR** the crumb mixture into the bottom of the pan and press down firmly to make a crust.

2. In a blender or food processor, **COMBINE** the cream cheese, Splenda, cinnamon, and vanilla. **BLEND** until fairly smooth. Add the pumpkin puree and blend until smooth, scraping down the sides as necessary. **ADD** the eggs and egg whites and **BLEND** about 15 to 20 seconds, until well combined but not frothy. You don't want to incorporate too much air into the batter, as your cheesecake will puff up in the oven then sink when it cools.

3. **POUR** the batter into the prepared pan. Firmly but carefully bang the bottom of the pan on the counter to get rid of any air bubbles. **BAKE** 35 to 40 minutes, until the cheesecake is set. The middle should be wobbly but not soupy (it should wiggle a bit when you shake the pan). Note: The cheesecake will continue to cook for up to 20 minutes outside the oven. **CHILL** the cheesecake for at least 3 hours in the refrigerator before trying to cut it.

4. Serve chilled and garnished with a tablespoon of light whipped topping and a sprinkling of cinnamon, if desired.

Pumpkin cheesecake NUTRITIONAL VALUE PER SERVING			
Calories	150	Total Fat	10g
Carbohydrates	10g	Saturated Fat	4g
Protein	7g	Cholesterol	95mg
Fiber	1g	Sodium	170mg

Exchanges: ½ carbohydrate, 1 vegetable, ½ medium-fat meat, 1 fat
Carb Choices: ½

quick berry crumble crisp

Part crumble and part crisp—this dessert is a superfast way to top off any meal

INGREDIENTS

1 16-ounce bag frozen mixed berry medley, thawed

1/2 cup Splenda

1 teaspoon lemon juice

1 cup oats

1/8 cup nuts, chopped (walnuts or pecans)

1 tablespoon all-purpose flour

1/2 teaspoon ground cinnamon

3 tablespoons butter or margarine

Cooking spray

1. **PREHEAT** oven to 350°F. **COMBINE** the thawed berries and all their juices, half of the Splenda, and the lemon juice. **MIX** well and pour into a 1.5-quart baking dish.

2. **PULSE** the oats and nuts in a blender to coarsely break up. **ADD** the remaining Splenda, flour, and cinnamon and pulse again.

3. **POUR** the oat mixture into a small bowl. **WORK** the butter into the oats with the tips of your fingers. The texture will be like coarse sawdust.

4. **COVER** the berries with the oat topping. Coat lightly with cooking spray. **BAKE** 30 minutes, until browned and bubbly. Serve warm with a dollop of light whipped topping or a small scoop of vanilla ice cream.

NUTRITIONAL VALUE PER SERVING

Calories	330	Total Fat	14g
Carbohydrates	45g	Saturated Fat	6g
Protein	8g	Cholesterol	25mg
Fiber	9g	Sodium	0mg

Exchanges: 1 1/2 carbohydrates, 2 fruits, 2 fats
Carb Choices: 3

last-minute macaroons

Moist, delicious, and ready in a flash, these are great for unexpected visitors

Serves: Makes 16 macaroons
Prep Time: 5 minutes
Cooking Time: 12-15 minutes

INGREDIENTS

2 extra-large egg whites

7 ounces lightly sweetened coconut, shredded

3 tablespoons Splenda

1/4 teaspoon vanilla or cherry extract

Cooking spray

1. PREHEAT oven to 350°F. In a small bowl, mix together all ingredients.

2. SPOON 16 macaroons onto a nonstick cookie sheet lined with parchment paper. If you don't have parchment paper, lightly spray cookie sheet with cooking oil spray. Use a small ice cream scoop or melon-baller to make uniform macaroons.

3. BAKE 12 to 15 minutes, until golden brown on the edges. **COOL** before serving.

NUTRITIONAL VALUE PER COOKIE			
Calories	90	Total Fat	7g
Carbohydrates	5g	Saturated Fat	6g
Protein	1g	Cholesterol	0mg
Fiber	1g	Sodium	30mg

Exchanges: 1/2 carbohydrate, 1 fat
Carb Choices: 1/2

cocoa chocolate brownies

Rich, chocolaty, and moist, these have a fraction of the sugar and fat of regular brownies

Makes: 16 brownies

Prep Time: 10 minutes

Cooking Time: 25-30 minutes

INGREDIENTS

2 ounces unsweetened chocolate

1/2 cup all-purpose flour

1/2 cup cocoa powder

1/8 teaspoon salt

2 eggs

1/2 cup Splenda

1/2 cup low-fat sour cream

1/4 cup cold water

2 tablespoons vegetable oil

2 tablespoons sugar

1 teaspoon vanilla extract

1/4 cup semisweet chocolate chips

1. PREHEAT oven to 350°F. Grease an 8 by 8 baking pan with margarine or butter. MELT the unsweetened chocolate over a double boiler or in a microwave oven, checking every 30 seconds to avoid burning it.

2. COMBINE the flour, cocoa powder, and salt in a bowl.

3. In a separate bowl, thoroughly MIX the eggs, Splenda, sour cream, water, oil, sugar, and vanilla. ADD the melted chocolate and mix well.

4. ADD the flour mixture. MIX well. The batter will be quite stiff. Add the chocolate chips.

5. Spread the batter in the prepared pan. BAKE for 25 to 30 minutes. Cool 10 minutes before cutting into 16 brownies.

NUTRITIONAL VALUE PER BROWNIE			
Calories	100	Total Fat	6g
Carbohydrates	11g	Saturated Fat	3g
Protein	3g	Cholesterol	30mg
Fiber	2g	Sodium	30mg

Exchanges: 1 carbohydrate, 1 fat
Carb Choices: 1

First Person Disaster: *Chocolate Cravings*

Since my son developed Type I diabetes, I've tried my best to make tasty desserts, especially on special occasions. I'm pretty good at adjusting recipes to lower the carbohydrates, but I haven't had much luck with chocolate desserts. Sugar-free sweeteners really seem to leave an "aftertaste" when baked with chocolate. I've finally figured out that if I leave in about 2 tablespoons of the sugar in the original recipe and substitute Splenda for the rest, I get a better result than removing all the sugar. The texture of the dessert is improved and the aftertaste is minimized without having to add a huge amount of sugar. I've also noticed that unsweetened baking chocolate (melted) often tastes better with sugar-free sweeteners than cocoa does. Where possible, I make that substitution too, even though the block chocolate has more fat in it than the cocoa. Finally, I've found that the best sugar-free chocolate desserts are the uncooked ones—frozen desserts, puddings, or sauces that can be sweetened off the heat. Who says you can't have your chocolate and eat it, too?

—Randy B., Gadsden, AL

bananas Foster

This buttery, brown-sugary, New Orleans classic will make your guests smile

Serves: 4

Prep Time: 5 minutes

Cooking Time: 6-8 minutes

INGREDIENTS

3 medium bananas, ripe

2 tablespoons butter or margarine

3 tablespoons Splenda

1 teaspoon ground cinnamon

1 tablespoon brown sugar

1 teaspoon banana extract

2 tablespoons light rum

2 cups low-fat vanilla ice cream, scooped into 4 perfect balls

1. Have all your ingredients ready because this does not take long to cook. PEEL the bananas. CUT them in half lengthwise, then in half across the middle.

2. In a medium sauté pan, MELT the butter over medium heat. ADD the bananas and BROWN them, turning gently, about 2 minutes. Add the Splenda, cinnamon, and brown sugar. Shake the pan to mix.

3. ADD the banana extract. Remove the pan from the flame. Add the rum. Return the pan to the heat and swirl the pan to combine. COOK another minute to evaporate the alcohol.

4. POUR the delicious, hot banana mixture over 1/2-cup balls of vanilla ice cream. Serve at once.

NUTRITIONAL VALUE PER SERVING			
Calories	280	Total Fat	8g
Carbohydrates	45g	Saturated Fat	4.5g
Protein	4g	Cholesterol	20mg
Fiber	3g	Sodium	50mg

Exchanges: 2 carbohydrates, 1 fruit, 1 1/2 fats
Carb Choices: 3

All you need are bananas, a bit of rum, and banana extract, and this
New Orleans classic is yours to make.

banana meringue pudding pie

A cross between pudding and meringue pie, this dessert is sure to please

Serves: 8

Prep Time: 20 minutes

Cooking Time: 10-15 minutes

Chilling Time: at least 30 minutes

INGREDIENTS

Cooking spray

28 low-fat vanilla wafer cookies

3 ripe bananas, peeled and sliced

2 egg yolks

3/4 cup Splenda

1/4 cup cornstarch

1 teaspoon banana extract

1 teaspoon vanilla extract

2 cups milk

1 teaspoon butter or margarine

4 egg whites

1. **PREHEAT** oven to 400°F. Lightly **COAT** a 9-inch glass pie pan with cooking spray. **LINE** the bottom and sides of the pie pan with the vanilla wafer cookies. Set aside. Put sliced bananas into a bowl and set aside.

2. In a medium-sized bowl, thoroughly **WHISK** the egg yolks, 1/2 cup Splenda, cornstarch, banana extract, and vanilla extract.

3. **HEAT** the milk in a saucepan over medium-high heat. Be careful not to let it boil over. When the milk is steaming and small bubbles have formed around the edges of the pan, **LADLE** a scoop of hot milk into the egg mixture, whisking as you pour. Ladle another spoonful of hot milk into the egg mixture and whisk. (This is called tempering the eggs, and it prevents the eggs from scrambling.) **POUR** the tempered egg mixture back into the hot milk and **WHISK** vigorously and continuously. The custard will thicken quickly, about 2 minutes. **WHISK** in butter. Remove from heat.

4. **POUR** the custard over the sliced bananas and mix well. Pour the banana-custard into the wafer-lined pie pan. **COVER** the surface with plastic wrap to prevent a skin from forming while you make the meringue.

5. With a handheld electric mixer on low, begin beating the egg whites (add a dash of cream of tartar for extra fluffiness, see page 181). When they're foamy, increase the mixer speed. Gradually **ADD** the remaining Splenda and **BEAT** until the egg whites are fluffy, hold peaks, and have a satiny shine.

6. Mound the egg whites on top of the pie and **SPREAD** to the edges. Try to keep the middle mounded high, but make sure to spread meringue over the edges of the pie to seal in moisture. **BAKE** 10 minutes until nicely browned, turning halfway through if your oven cooks unevenly. The meringue should be crispy to the touch but soft in the middle. **REFRIGERATE** until ready to serve.

what do I do now?

FOLDING

If you've got a very fluffy substance, say whipped cream or meringue, and you have to add it to a denser substance, like a custard, "folding" allows you to gently mix them without deflating the fluffy ingredient. A large rubber spatula is the best tool for the job. Just take about ½ of the fluffy substance and gently stir it into the thicker one to lighten it. Then add the rest of the fluffy substance and gently fold through the middle of the mixture. At the bottom of the bowl, pull the spatula toward you and up the side of the bowl. Gently continue this motion, using your other hand to slowly turn the bowl.

Folding a dry substance into a fluffy one, as with our sponge cake recipe (see page 176), uses the same principles. Just make sure the dry ingredients are sifted, and add them a little bit at a time. It helps to sift them onto a sheet of wax paper first so you can easily control how much you add. And remember, don't overmix.

Banana meringue pudding pie
NUTRITIONAL VALUE PER SERVING

Calories	190	Total Fat	6g
Carbohydrates	28g	Saturated Fat	2.5g
Protein	6g	Cholesterol	70mg
Fiber	1g	Sodium	105mg

Exchanges: 1½ carbohydrates, ½ fruit, 1 fat
Carb Choices: 2

chocolate banana parcels

These crispy, flaky bundles of chocolate banana goodness are ready in a flash

Serves: 4

Prep Time: 15 minutes

Cooking Time: 12-15 minutes

INGREDIENTS

½ tablespoon sugar

1 teaspoon cocoa powder

3-4 sheets phyllo pastry

Cooking spray, preferably butter-flavored

2 ripe medium bananas, peeled and quartered

1 Hershey's chocolate bar (or scant ¼ cup chocolate chips)

1. **PREHEAT** oven to 350°F. In a small bowl, **MIX** the sugar and cocoa.

2. **LAY** 1 sheet of phyllo dough on a clean, flat surface. **COAT** lightly with cooking spray. Sprinkle lightly with ½ teaspoon of the cocoa mixture. **LAYER** 2 to 3 more sheets of phyllo over the first, lightly coating each with cooking spray and the cocoa mixture.

3. With a sharp knife, **CUT** the phyllo into 4 equal rectangles. Lay 2 pieces of banana in the middle of each section of phyllo. **PLACE** ¼ of the chocolate bar or 1 tablespoon of chocolate chips with the banana.

4. **PULL** the corners and sides of the phyllo up around the bananas and chocolate. Gently twist the dough to seal the pouch. It should look like a little change purse.

5. **PLACE** the parcels on a cookie sheet lightly coated with cooking spray. Lightly **COAT** the parcels with cooking spray and sprinkle with a little remaining cocoa mixture. **BAKE** 12 to 15 minutes, until golden and crisp. Serve warm on its own or with a ¼-cup scoop of vanilla ice cream for an extra special dessert, if desired.

NUTRITIONAL VALUE PER SERVING			
Calories	170	Total Fat	5g
Carbohydrates	32g	Saturated Fat	2.5g
Protein	3g	Cholesterol	0mg
Fiber	2g	Sodium	10mg

Exchanges: 1 carbohydrate, 1 fruit, 1 fat
Carb Choices: 2

DIABETES AND CHOCOLATE

Chocolate, as in candy bars, cake, and icing, can be part of a healthy diet if eaten in small portions. Chocolate per se isn't bad for you, but traditional chocolate desserts come with lots of extra sugar and saturated fat. If you are eating out, be sure to split a single chocolate dessert with your spouse or kids. Just a taste of a chocolaty treat can often satisfy the biggest chocolate craving.

At home, you can make your own tempting chocolate treats. Use cocoa or unsweetened baking chocolate to create delicious desserts. They still contain fat in the form of cocoa butter, but they don't contain sugar. One tip is to buy Dutch process cocoa, which has a more mellow flavor than regular cocoa. You can pair these unsweetened chocolates with a noncaloric sweetener like Splenda in baking. For a quick chocolate boost, try making this sauce. It's great over ½ cup of vanilla ice cream or for dipping fresh fruit.

EASY CHOCOLATE SAUCE

¼ cup cocoa

¼ cup + 1 tablespoon Splenda

½ cup water

½ teaspoon vanilla

1. COMBINE all the ingredients in a small saucepan over medium-high heat. STIR well until smooth. Cool slightly. Serve over reduced fat ice cream or fresh fruit. Makes ¾ cup chocolate sauce.

Easy chocolate sauce
NUTRITIONAL VALUE PER TABLESPOON

Calories	5	Total Fat	0g
Carbohydrates	2g	Saturated Fat	0g
Protein	0g	Cholesterol	0mg
Fiber	0g	Sodium	0mg

glossary

"**Across the grain**" refers to slicing meats perpendicular to the long bundles of muscle that run through the meat. This produces tender slices that are easier to chew.

Alfredo sauce is a 1920s classic made from butter, Parmesan cheese, heavy cream, and lots of black pepper. It can be lightened by using light margarine, cornstarch, and milk instead of heavy cream.

Baking powder is a familiar leavening agent for quick bread, cakes, biscuits, and muffins. One-fourth teaspoon baking soda plus ⁵/₈ teaspoon cream of tartar can be substituted for 1 teaspoon of baking powder.

Baking soda is also known as bicarbonate of soda. It's a common leavening in baking. When baking soda is combined with an acidic ingredient such as vinegar, yogurt, molasses, or buttermilk, bubbles of carbon dioxide are formed, making baked goods rise.

Bean threads, also called cellophane noodles, are thin, translucent, or transparent noodles made from starch found in mung beans. They are sold dried in bundles and should be soaked for a few minutes in hot water before cooking or using in salads. They are also excellent in soups, and need not be presoaked for this. They can be found in Asian grocery stores and often in large supermarkets.

Bisque is a thick, rich soup usually made of pureed seafood, vegetables, or poultry and thickened with cream. The calories in bisque can be reduced by substituting a few teaspoons of cornstarch, mixed with milk, for the cream.

Black bean sauce or paste is a salty, pungent flavoring made from salt-preserved black soybeans. It is a common ingredient in Chinese cooking. It can be found in the Asian section of many large grocery stores or in Asian markets. Be aware that the sodium content is quite high, and a little goes a long way.

Boston or bibb lettuce *See* **Butter lettuce**

Braise means to cook meats or vegetables by first browning very well, then slowly simmering in liquid, usually broth, tightly covered with a lid. Braising can be done in a relatively low-heat oven (no more than 350°F) or on the stove top.

Bran is the outer husk of grains, such as wheat, rice, or oats, that is typically removed during processing at a mill. Whole-grain breads, brown rice, and raw oats that are minimally processed contain more bran than refined baked goods (like white bread, pasta, and white rice). Bran contributes important fiber to the diet, as well as carbohydrates and minerals, and should be added to your meals in the form of cereals and whole-grain products.

Butter lettuce includes Boston and bibb lettuces. It's a delicious, mildly sweet lettuce with tender, pale-green leaves. The loosely packed heads can be cut in half or quartered to add interesting structure to meal salads. Individual leaves are delicious on sandwiches.

Capsaicin is the chemical in peppers that gives them their "heat." Capsaicin is concentrated in the seeds and white, spongy ribs of hot peppers. Handle these parts carefully and do not touch your eyes or nose if you've been working with hot peppers.

Caramelize means to brown sugar, whether refined table sugar or sugars in fruits and vegetables. Caramelization adds sweetness, color, and depth of flavor to dishes, from desserts to soups and sauces.

Cassoulet is a classic, slow-cooked, French stew featuring bold meats, such as pork, sausage, or duck, white beans, and often some sort of bread-crumb topping.

Cellophane noodles *See* **bean thread**

Cilantro is also known as Chinese parsley or fresh coriander. It has a pungent, peppery flavor that can be quite overwhelming. Cilantro is common in Asian, Caribbean, and Latin American cuisine. Chopped cilantro, thoroughly cleaned, can be frozen and used effectively in cooked dishes.

Chili powder is a popular spice mix used in Tex-Mex recipes. It consists of powdered dried chili peppers, garlic, cumin, oregano, coriander, and cloves. Some chili seasoning mixes contain salt, so check the label to avoid oversalting.

Clementines, together with satsumas and tangerines, are considered Mandarin oranges. These varieties are all small, sweet, easily peeled, and practically seedless.

Couscous is a grainlike pasta from North Africa. Found packaged in most grocery stores and in bulk in many natural food stores, it cooks in about 5 minutes when added to boiling water or broth.

Cream of tartar is a fine, white, acidic powder that reacts with baking soda in baking powder. It is often added to candies and frosting to make them creamier. Cream of tartar added to egg whites before beating makes them fluffier and more stable in meringues and soufflés.

Crudités are raw vegetables, trimmed and cut, typically served with a dipping sauce and enjoyed as an appetizer or snack. *Crudité* comes from the French word for "rawness."

Cumin is a bold, aromatic spice with a slightly earthy and nutty flavor. It comes in seed form or ground into powder. It is often toasted before using to bring out extra flavor. Cumin is an important ingredient in curries and chili powders. It is widely used in Middle Eastern, Asian, Mexican, and Mediterranean cooking.

Dark soy sauce is made from fermented soybeans and wheat or barley. Dark soy sauce is less salty and has a richer flavor and thicker consistency than the more familiar light soy sauce. Dark soy sauce gives more color to dishes where this is desirable.

Dash is a colloquial measuring term that generally refers to an amount between $1/16$ and a scant $1/8$ of a teaspoon.

Devein means to remove the gray-black intestinal vein that runs down the back of a shrimp. Small and medium shrimp need not be deveined. Large shrimp should be deveined, either before or after cooking, because the vein often contains grit that can be unpleasant to eat.

Dice means to cut food into $1/8$- to $1/4$-inch cubes. Most recipes will say to dice large, medium, or small pieces.

Emulsify is to combine liquids that normally separate, such as vinegar and oil. This is accomplished by slowly adding one liquid to the other and whisking continuously to suspend minute droplets of one throughout the other. Emulsifiers like mustard or vegetable purees help keep the liquids combined. Mayonnaise, classic hollandaise sauce, and creamy vinaigrettes are common examples of emulsified mixtures.

English cucumbers, also called European cucumbers, are longer, thinner, and sweeter than regular cucumbers. They have a very thin skin and practically no seeds. They are usually sold individually shrink-wrapped.

Extra-lean meats, as defined by the U.S. Department of Agriculture, contain less than 5 grams of fat per 3-ounce serving.

Fat-free foods, as defined by the U.S. Food and Drug Administration, contain less than $1/2$ gram of fat per serving, providing there are no added fats or oils.

Fold means to gently combine a light, airy mixture (such as beaten egg whites) with a heavier mixture (such as whipped cream or custard). A little of the lighter mixture is blended into the heavier one to lighten it. Then the rest of the light ingredient is placed on top of the heavier one. A rubber spatula is used to cut down vertically through the two mixtures, then it is pulled across the bottom of the bowl and up toward you. The bowl should be rotated with your free hand until the two mixtures are combined with as little deflation as possible.

Garde-manger is a French term used in large professional kitchens that refers to the area where cool foods such as salads, patés, terrines, and hors d'oeuvres are prepared. The person in charge of this area is called the chef garde-manger.

Herbes de Provence is the name for a mix of dried herbs that are common along France's southern coast. Herbes de Provence typically contains thyme, basil, marjoram, rosemary, sage, and fennel seed. Other herbs, such as lavender, savory, tarragon, and chervil, can be added. A hint of ground clove and orange zest are included in some blends as well.

Hoisin sauce is salty-sweet and flavored with garlic and Chinese five-spice. It is available in the international section of most grocery stores, near the soy sauce. It should be used sparingly because of its high sugar and salt content.

Hummus is a thick Middle Eastern sauce or dip made from pureed chickpeas, lemon juice, olive oil, garlic, and tahini (sesame paste).

Jicama is a crunchy, sweet root vegetable, sometimes called a Mexican potato. Widely available in the produce section of supermarkets, jicama should be peeled before eating.

Lean meat, as defined by the U.S. Department of Agriculture, contains less than 10 grams of fat per 3-ounce serving.

Leeks are large, mild-flavored members of the onion family. Delicious in soups and stews, and sautéed, roasted, or raw in salads, leeks must be well cleaned before cooking because the tightly layered leaves trap dirt.

Legumes are plants that produce seed pods that split along both sides when ripe. Dried beans (often referred to as "pules"), lentils, peanuts, peas, and soybeans are common examples of this category of nutritious foods.

Low-calorie, as defined by the U.S. Food and Drug Administration, means 40 calories or less per serving.

Low-fat, as defined by the U.S. Food and Drug Administration, means the amount of fat per serving (3 ounces, or 100 grams, of food) is 3 grams or less.

Marinate is to soak meat, fish, or vegetables in a seasoned liquid mixture called a marinade. Marinating foods helps them absorb flavor and, if an acidic ingredient is used, tenderizes them. Marinate in a nonreactive container like glass, stainless steel, or ceramic. Meats marinated longer than 30 minutes should be kept in the refrigerator. Used marinating liquid (marinade) generally should be discarded. In some cases, the used marinade can be boiled and strained for a sauce.

Meringue is a fluffy mixture of egg whites and sugar (or sweetener) beaten together until stiff. Meringue may be used to top pies and puddings, and then baked until browned but still soft and chewy in the middle. Meringue can also be piped onto parchment paper and baked for several hours in a very low-heat oven (200°F) until crunchy.

Monounsaturated fat is found chiefly in canola, olive, and peanut oils.

Napa cabbage, sometimes called Chinese cabbage, should not be confused with bok choy, another Chinese cabbage. Napa is light green and white. It comes in tightly packed, oblong heads. It's wonderful raw, in soups, or in stir-fry. When using it raw, peel away any limp outer layers that may be surrounding the crisp inner ones.

Phyllo pastry, sometimes called filo pastry, comes frozen in paper-thin sheets. It is used in Greek dishes such as baklava and spanakopita. It is low-fat and becomes very flaky when cooked. It should be covered with a kitchen towel while you're working with it and tightly wrapped in the refrigerator to prevent it from drying out.

Poach means to cook food gently in flavored liquid that is just below the boiling point. There should be virtually no surface action on the hot liquid, with bubbles forming only on the bottom of the pan or pot. Meats, fish, and poultry are usually poached in broth or stock of the same. Fruits are often poached in syrup or wine. And the common poached egg is cooked in salted water with a touch of vinegar.

Polenta is an Italian porridge made from cornmeal. Different grinds make for different textures of cooked polenta. Cheese is the most common flavoring in polenta, which can be eaten soft or cooled, cut into squares, and browned.

Polyunsaturated fat is found primarily in vegetable oils such as safflower, sunflower, corn, flaxseed, and canola. Polyunsaturated fats are also the main fats found in seafood. They are liquid or soft at room temperature. "Essential fatty acids" are part of the polyunsaturated family and are important for maintaining cells and making hormones.

Ramekin is an individual ceramic baking dish that resembles a miniature soufflé dish. It is great for any sort of entree (such as potpies or gratins) or dessert (cobblers, custards, flan), served hot or cold. Heatproof earthenware or porcelain cups can be substituted. Ramekins make beautiful meal presentations. They also allow for strict portion control of rich foods.

Reduce in cooking terms means to concentrate flavors of liquid (usually a stock, sauce, or wine) by rapidly boiling it. The more water that evaporates, the less liquid in the pot and the stronger the flavor created.

Reduced-calorie foods, as defined by the U.S. Food and Drug Administration, contain at least $1/3$ fewer calories than the regular product.

Reduced-fat foods, as defined by the U.S. Food and Drug Administration, contain 50% or less fat than the regular product.

Remoulade is a mayonnaise-based sauce, usually mixed with mustard, herbs, and other aromatic ingredients. It's a French classic generally served with seafood or chilled meats.

Render is to melt away the fat from a piece of meat, using either the stove top or the oven.

Roast means to cook food in an uncovered pan in the oven. Fairly tender cuts of meat are well suited to roasting and will produce a nicely browned surface while remaining juicy. Less tender cuts are better braised.

Saturated fat is found mainly in animal proteins, including whole-fat dairy products. Saturated fats are generally solid at room temperature. If consumed in great amounts, they can contribute to heart disease and high blood pressure. It should be noted that coconut and palm oils also contain saturated fat.

Sear means to brown meat in a skillet, under a broiler, or in a very hot oven. Whether searing actually seals in meat juices for a more tender dish is a controversial topic. However, all agree that searing adds flavor and color to the finished dish.

Silverskin is the tough, iridescent connective tissue around certain cuts of meat, most notably the tenderloin. It should be removed with a sharp knife before cooking to prevent bunching and uneven cooking.

Tahini is a thick sesame-seed paste used to flavor many Middle Eastern dishes, such as hummus.

Tofu is a low-fat, protein-rich food made from soybeans. Tofu is a popular ingredient in Chinese and Japanese cooking. It is extremely mildly flavored and has the ability to take on the flavor of the ingredients it's cooked with.

Vinaigrette is a basic combination of oil and vinegar generally used to dress salads or cold vegetable, meat, or fish dishes. Typical oil-vinegar proportions are 3 parts oil to 1 part vinegar. However, to reduce calories, use only a small amount of a high-quality, flavorful oil. Use broth or juice with the vinegar. Mustard, spices, herbs, shallots, onions, and pureed fruits or vegetables can be added to vary the flavor.

Watercress is a delicate, peppery green related to mustard greens. Its long tender stems and scalloped leaves should be rinsed gently to keep the leaves from falling off the stem.

index

about the author

Deborah Bone is a professional chef and caterer in New Orleans, Louisiana; North Carolina; and Virginia. Her entry into diabetic cooking began seven years ago when she met her husband, a Type 1 diabetic. After one of her tasty meals sent his blood sugar soaring, "I realized how important it was to understand exactly how different foods affect a diabetic." With that in mind, she set out to develop recipes and techniques that would help her husband control his blood sugar without sacrificing flavor. What she came up with is a fresh approach to old recipe favorites, using less salt, fat, and sugar. "It's just smart, healthy cooking for anyone. Controlling fat and calories and carbohydrates makes everyone feel better." Deborah lives in Virginia with her husband, Paul, to whom she dedicates this, her first, cookbook.

Barbara J. Morgan Publisher

Barnes & Noble Basics
Barb Chintz Editorial Director
Leonard Vigliarolo Design Director

Barnes & Noble Basics *Diabetes Cookbook*™
Judy Pray Editor
Mindy Hermann, R.D. Nutritional Consultant
Leslie Stem Design Assistant
Emily Seese Editorial Assistant
Della R. Mancuso Production Manager

ART CREDITS
Robert Milazzo All Major Food Photography
Megan Clark Photo Stylist

Corbis: 81, 115; **Digital Stock:** 10, 13, 15, 27, 39 (*top*), 59, 61, 65, 150, 169; **PhotoDisc:** 8, 17, 39 (*bottom*), 154, 185;
Sally Mara Sturman: 3, 44-45, 118